HUMAN BODY
COLORING BOOK

amber
BOOKS

Reprinted in 2023

First published in 2021

Published by
Amber Books Ltd
United House
North Road
London N7 9DP
United Kingdom
www.amberbooks.co.uk
Instagram: amberbooksltd
Facebook: amberbooks
Twitter: @amberbooks
Pinterest: amberbooksltd

ISBN 978-1-4351-6099-6

Printed in China

Contents

Front of skull

The skull is the head's natural crash helmet, protecting the brain and sense organs from damage. It is made up of 28 separate bones and is the most complex element of the human skeleton.

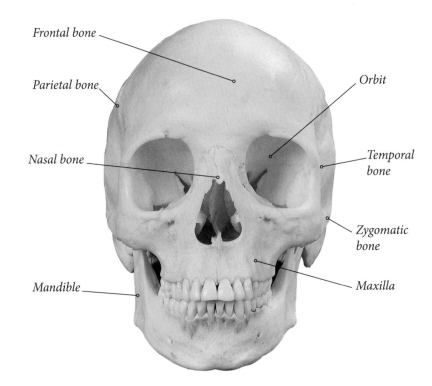

Frontal bone

Parietal bone

Nasal bone

Mandible

Orbit

Temporal bone

Zygomatic bone

Maxilla

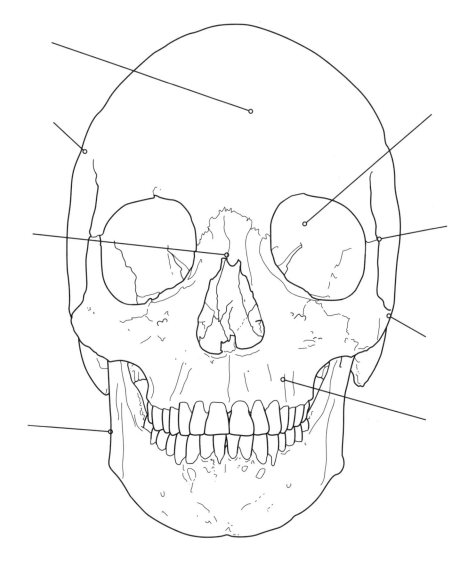

Side of skull

A lateral or side view of the skull clearly reveals the complexity of the structure, with many separate bones and the joints between them.

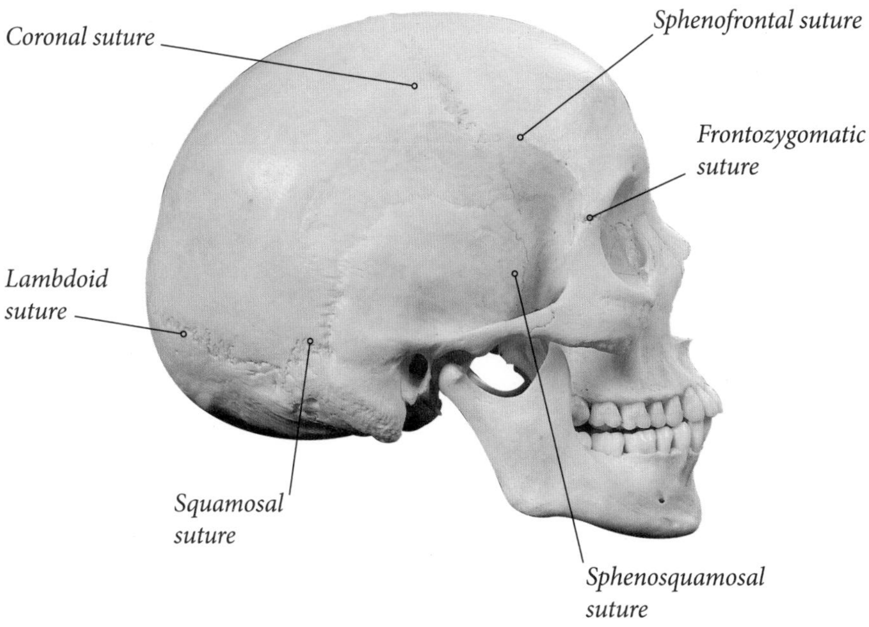

Coronal suture

Sphenofrontal suture

Frontozygomatic suture

Lambdoid suture

Squamosal suture

Sphenosquamosal suture

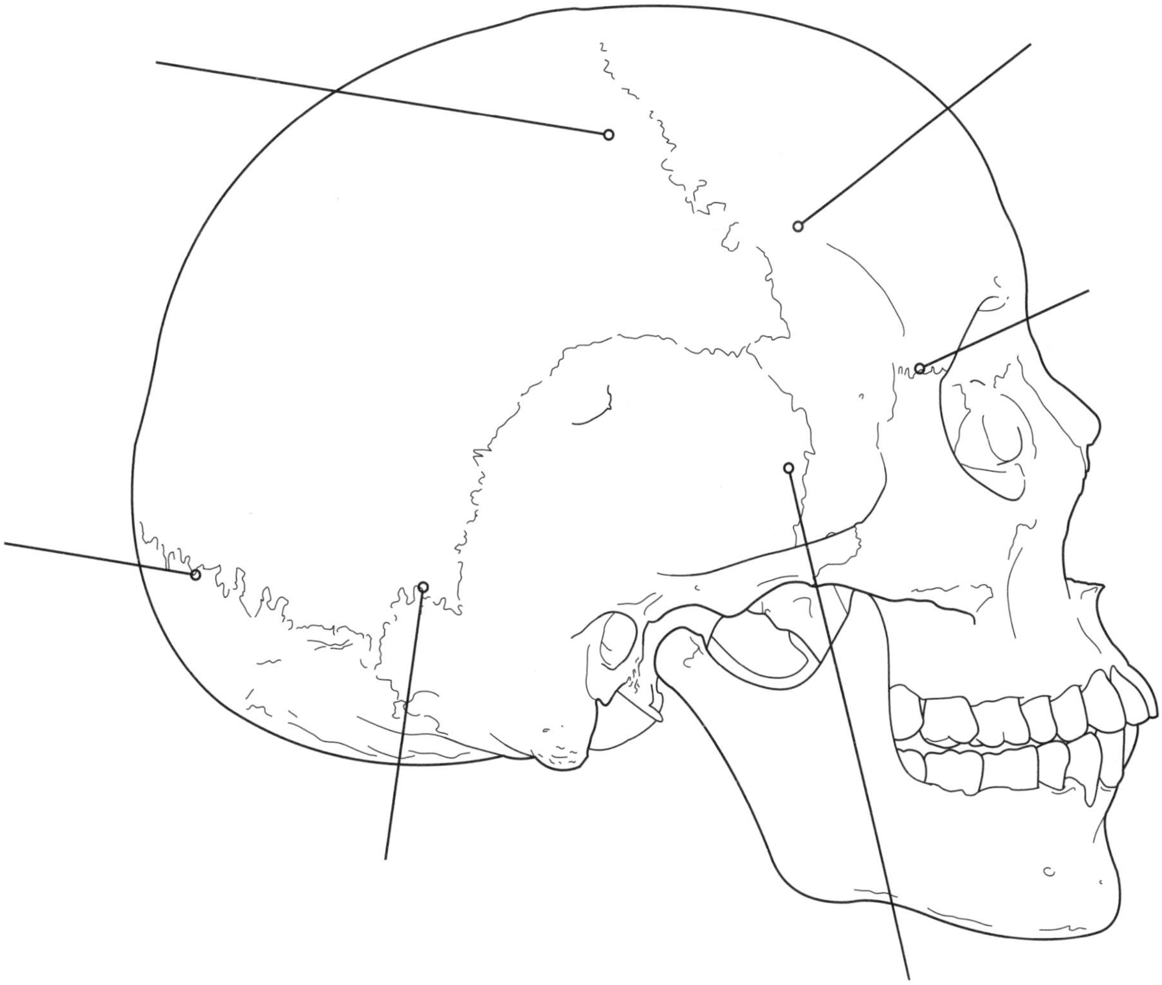

Base of skull

This unusual view of the skull is from below. The upper jaw and the hole through which the spinal cord goes can be seen.

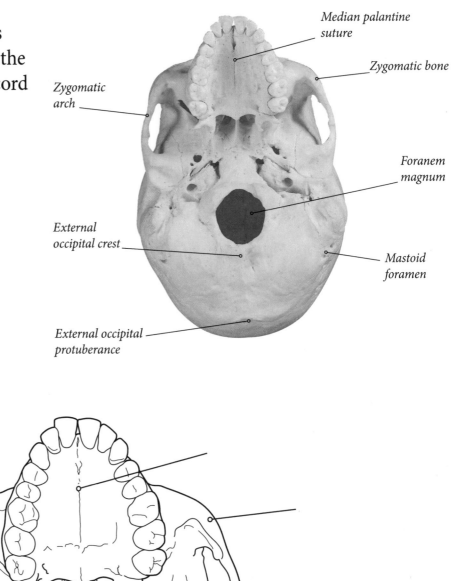

Median palantine suture

Zygomatic bone

Zygomatic arch

Foranem magnum

External occipital crest

Mastoid foramen

External occipital protuberance

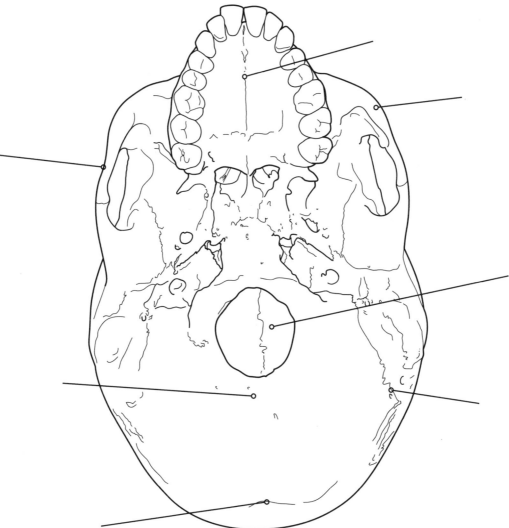

Scalp

The scalp is composed of five layers of tissue that cover the bones of the skull. The skin is firmly attached to the muscles of the scalp by connective tissue that also carries numerous blood vessels.

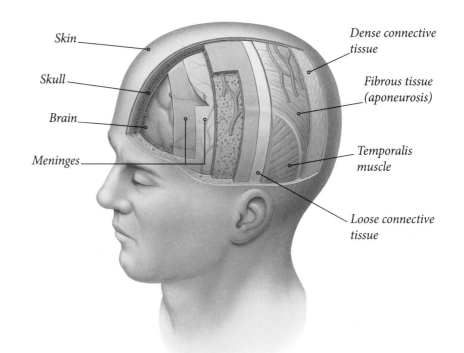

Skin

Skull

Brain

Meninges

Dense connective tissue

Fibrous tissue (aponeurosis)

Temporalis muscle

Loose connective tissue

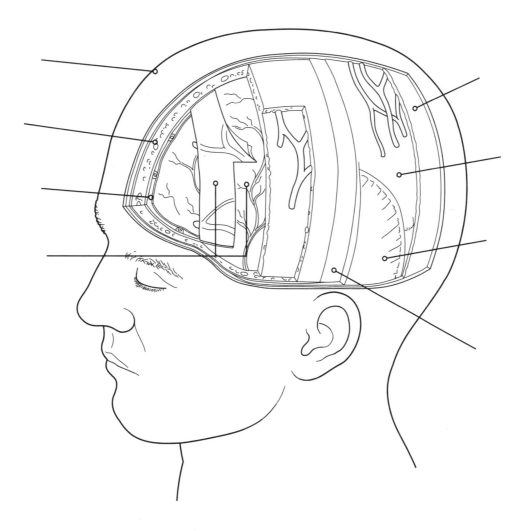

Muscles of the scalp

The muscles of the scalp lie below the skin and a layer of connective tissue. They act to move the skin of the forehead and the jaw while chewing.

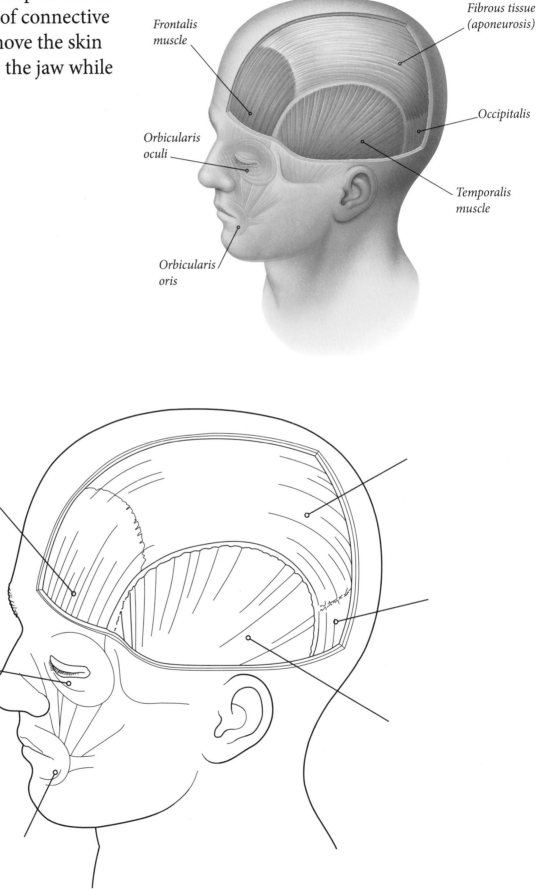

Frontalis muscle

Fibrous tissue (aponeurosis)

Orbicularis oculi

Occipitalis

Temporalis muscle

Orbicularis oris

Brain

The brain is the part of the central nervous system that lies inside the skull. It controls many body functions including our heart rate, the ability to walk and run, and the creation of our thoughts.

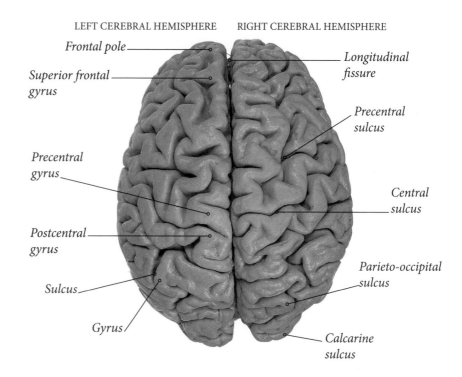

LEFT CEREBRAL HEMISPHERE   RIGHT CEREBRAL HEMISPHERE

Frontal pole

Superior frontal gyrus

Precentral gyrus

Postcentral gyrus

Sulcus

Gyrus

Longitudinal fissure

Precentral sulcus

Central sulcus

Parieto-occipital sulcus

Calcarine sulcus

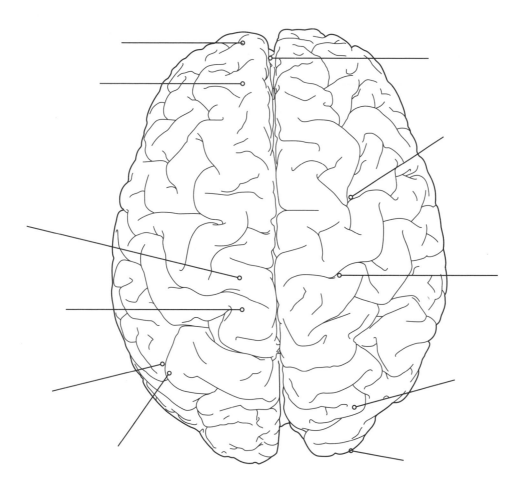

Inside the brain

A midline section between the two cerebral hemispheres reveals the main structures that control a vast number of activities in the body. While particular areas monitor sensory and motor information, others control speech and sleep.

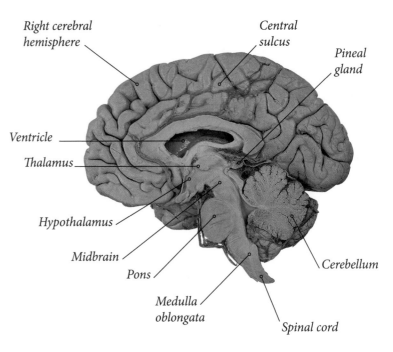

Right cerebral hemisphere

Central sulcus

Pineal gland

Ventricle

Thalamus

Hypothalamus

Midbrain

Pons

Medulla oblongata

Cerebellum

Spinal cord

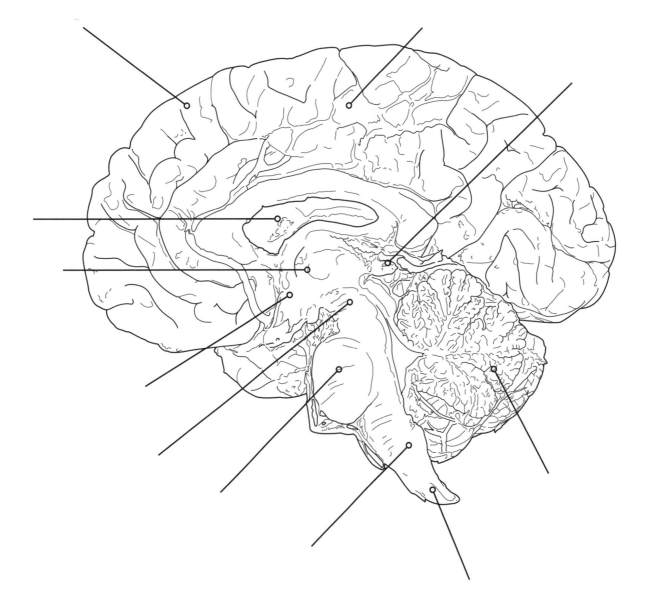

Blood vessels of the brain

The arteries provide the
brain with a rich supply of
oxygenated blood.

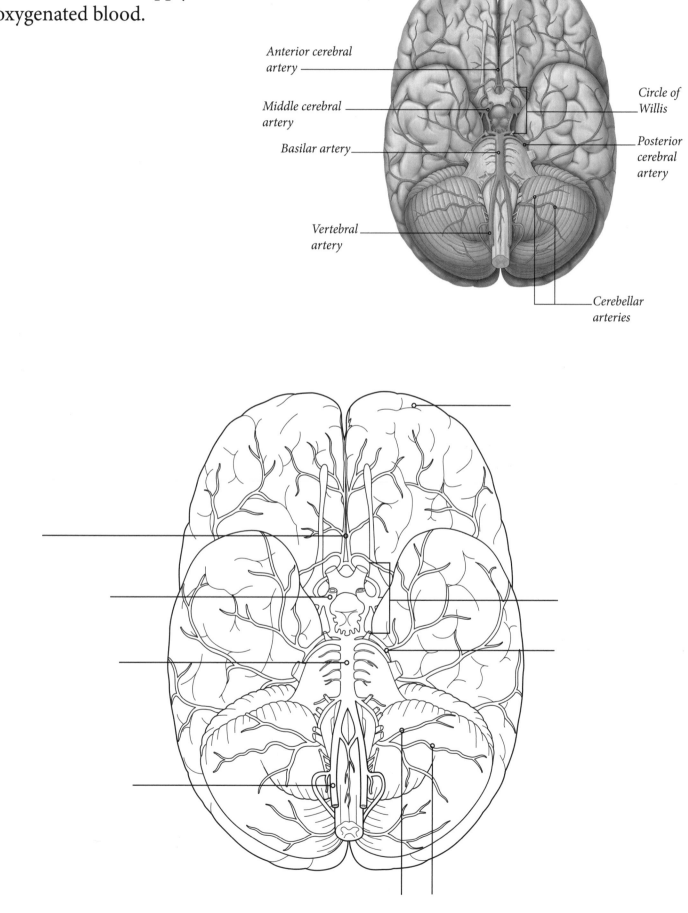

Cerebrum

Anterior cerebral
artery

Middle cerebral
artery

Basilar artery

Vertebral
artery

Circle of
Willis

Posterior
cerebral
artery

Cerebellar
arteries

Veins of the brain

The veins of the brain can be divided into deep and superficial groups. These veins, none of which have valves, drain into the venous sinuses of the skull.

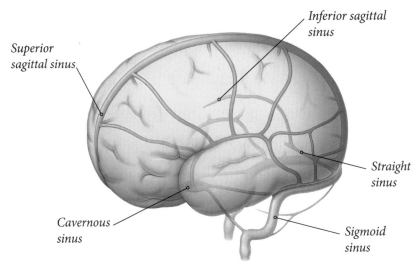

Superior sagittal sinus

Inferior sagittal sinus

Straight sinus

Cavernous sinus

Sigmoid sinus

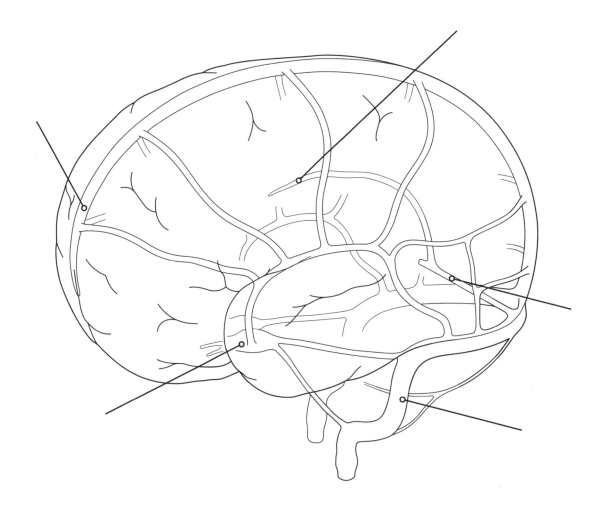

Cerebral hemispheres

The cerebral hemispheres are the largest part of the brain. In humans, they have developed out of proportion to the other regions, distinguishing our brains from those of other animals.

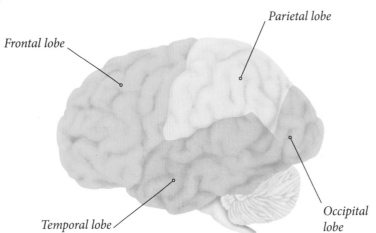

Frontal lobe

Parietal lobe

Occipital lobe

Temporal lobe

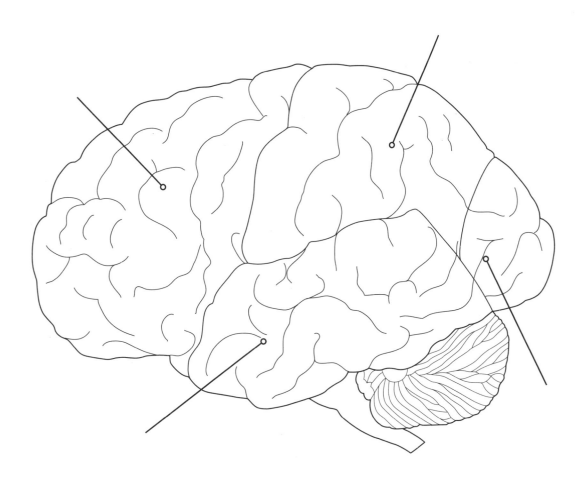

Functions of the cerebral hemispheres

Different regions of the cortex have distinct and highly specialized functions.

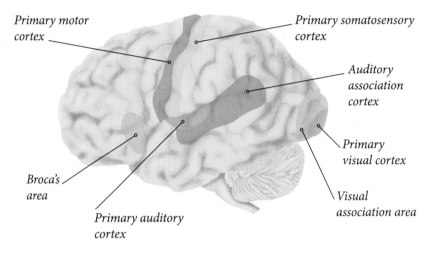

Primary motor cortex

Primary somatosensory cortex

Auditory association cortex

Primary visual cortex

Visual association area

Broca's area

Primary auditory cortex

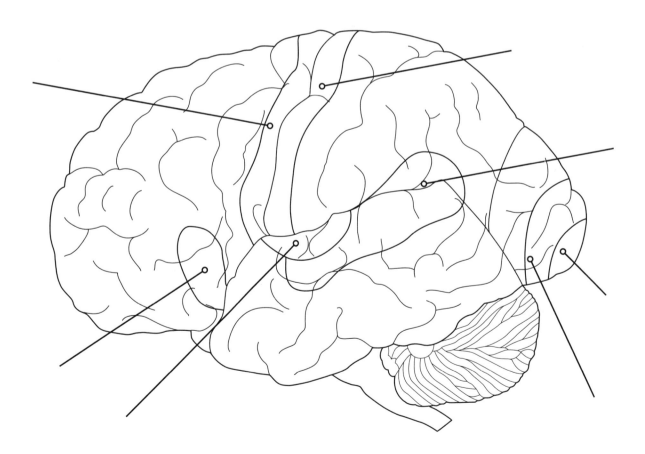

Thalamus

The thalamus is a major sensory relay and integrating center in the brain, lying deep within its central core. It consists of two halves, and receives sensory inputs of all types, except smell.

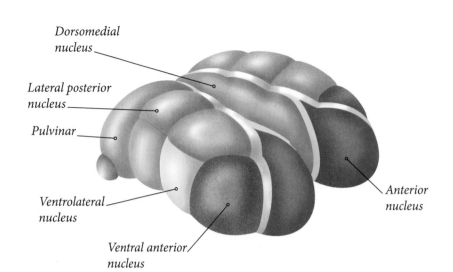

Dorsomedial nucleus

Lateral posterior nucleus

Pulvinar

Ventrolateral nucleus

Ventral anterior nucleus

Anterior nucleus

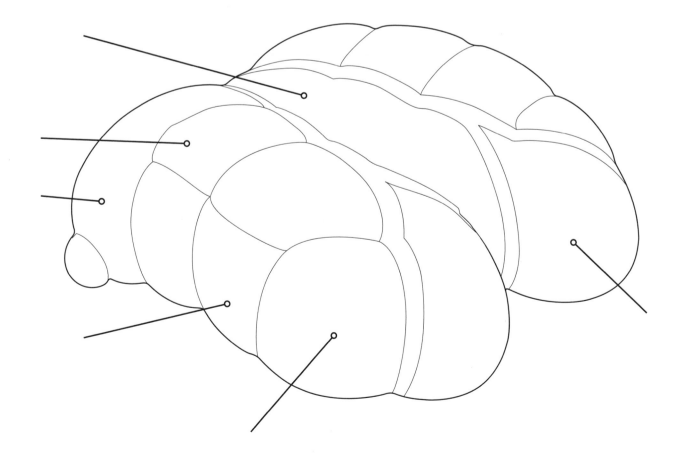

Hypothalamus

The hypothalamus is a complex structure located in the deep core of the brain. It regulates fundamental aspects of body function, and is critical for homeostasis—the maintenance of equilibrium in the body's internal environment.

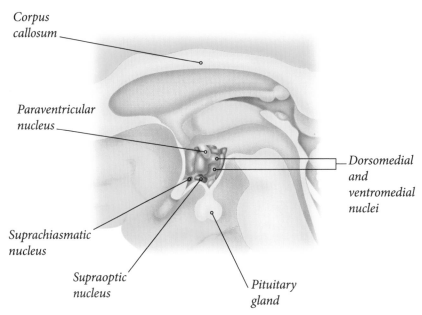

Corpus callosum

Paraventricular nucleus

Dorsomedial and ventromedial nuclei

Suprachiasmatic nucleus

Supraoptic nucleus

Pituitary gland

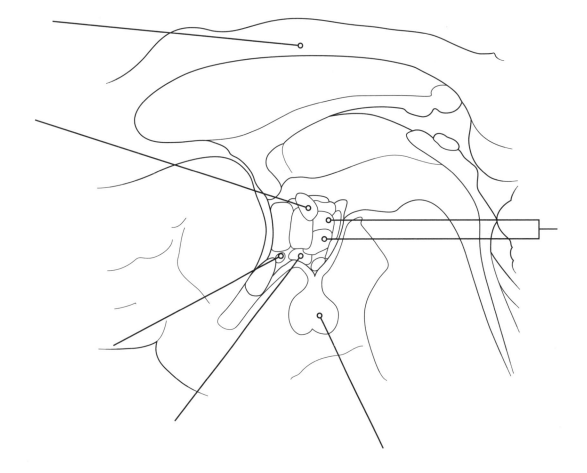

Limbic system

The limbic system is a ring of interconnected structures that lies deep within the brain. It makes connections with other parts of the brain and is associated with mood and memory.

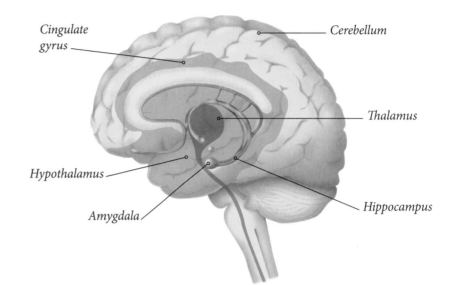

Cingulate gyrus

Cerebellum

Thalamus

Hypothalamus

Hippocampus

Amygdala

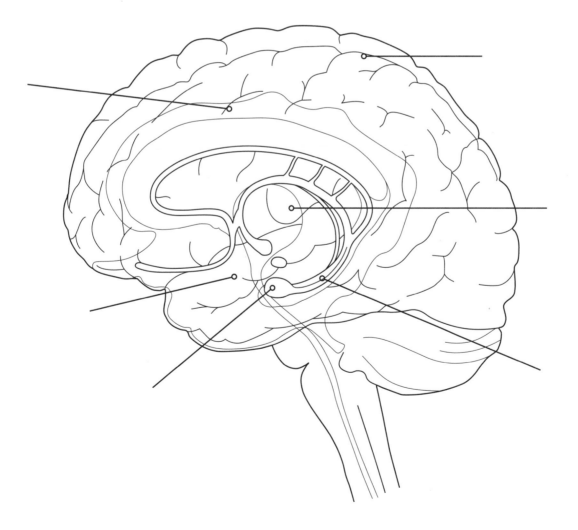

Basal ganglia

The basal ganglia lie deep within the white matter of the cerebral hemispheres. They are collections of nerve cell bodies that are involved in the control of movement.

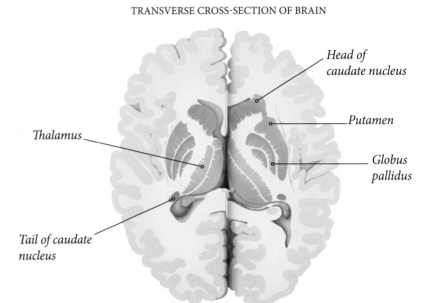

TRANSVERSE CROSS-SECTION OF BRAIN

Head of caudate nucleus

Putamen

Globus pallidus

Thalamus

Tail of caudate nucleus

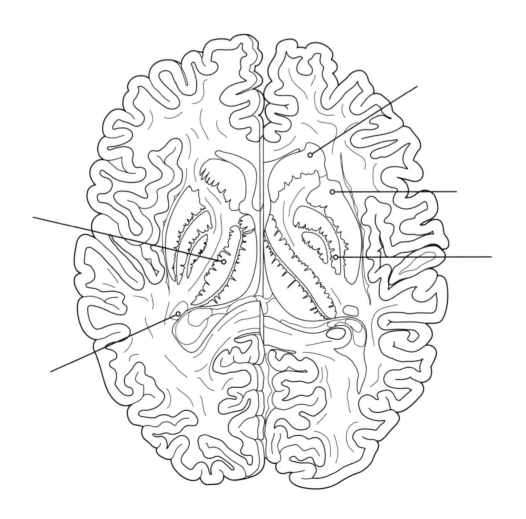

Structure and role of the basal ganglia

The overall shape of the basal ganglia (nuclei) is complex and is hard to imagine by looking at two-dimensional cross-sections.

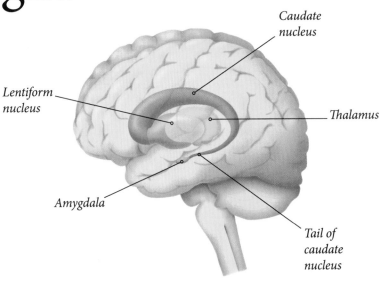

Caudate nucleus

Lentiform nucleus

Thalamus

Amygdala

Tail of caudate nucleus

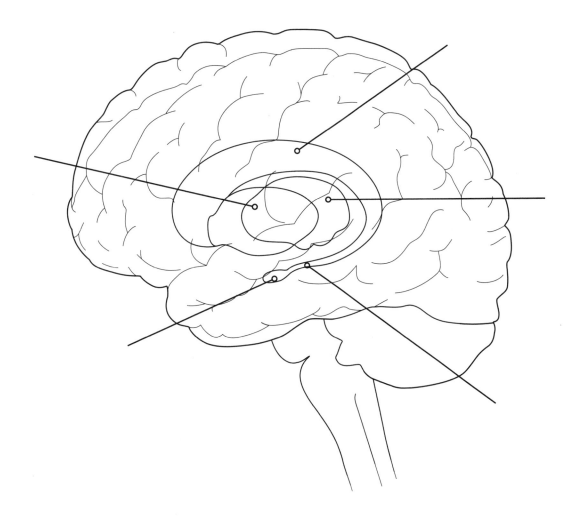

Cerebellum

The cerebellum, which means "little brain," lies under the occipital lobes of the cerebral cortex at the back of the brain. It is important to the subconscious control of movement.

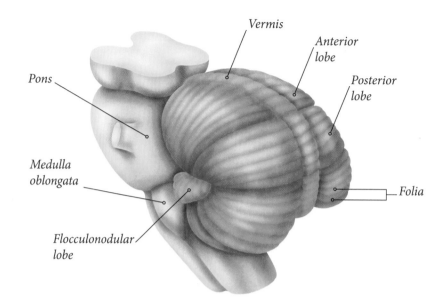

Vermis

Anterior lobe

Posterior lobe

Pons

Medulla oblongata

Flocculonodular lobe

Folia

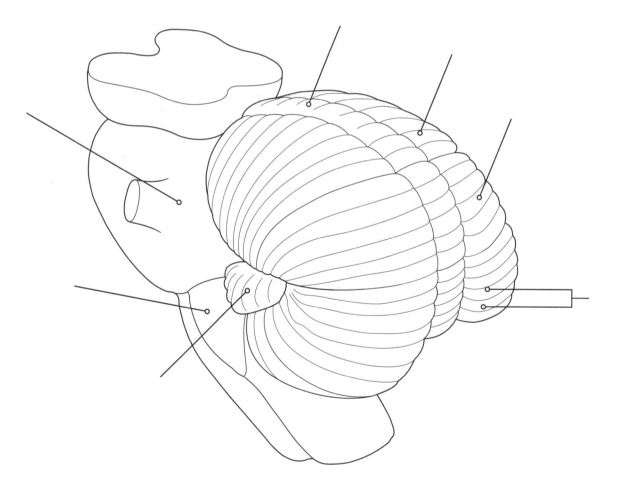

Internal structure of the cerebellum

The cerebellum has an outer gray cortex and a core of nerve fibers, or white matter. Deep within the white matter lie four pairs of cerebellar nuclei: the fastigial, globose, emboliform, and dentate nuclei.

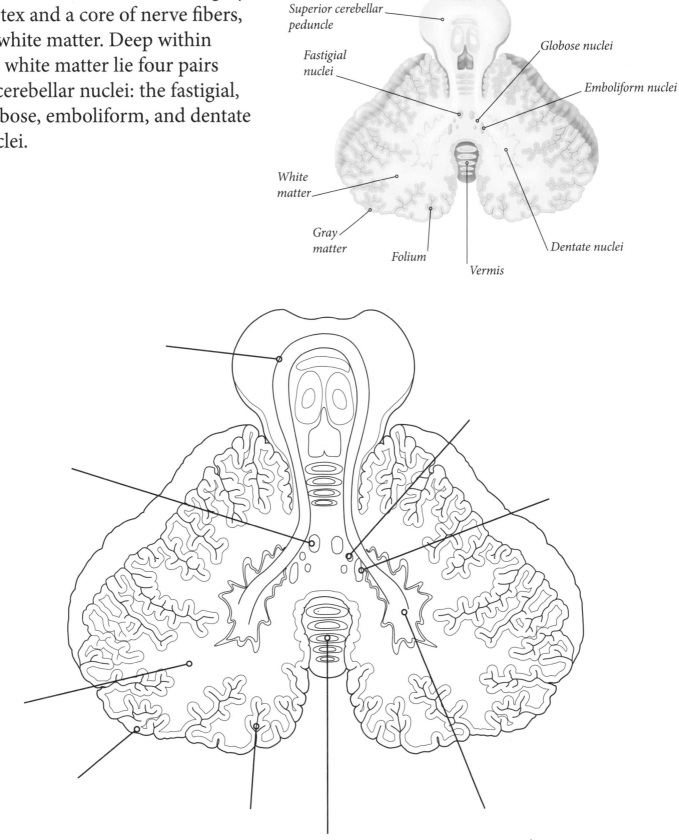

CROSS-SECTION OF CEREBELLUM

Superior cerebellar peduncle

Globose nuclei

Fastigial nuclei

Emboliform nuclei

White matter

Gray matter

Folium

Vermis

Dentate nuclei

Cranial nerves

There are twelve pairs of cranial nerves that leave the brain to supply structures mainly of the head and neck. The cranial nerves carry information to and from the brain.

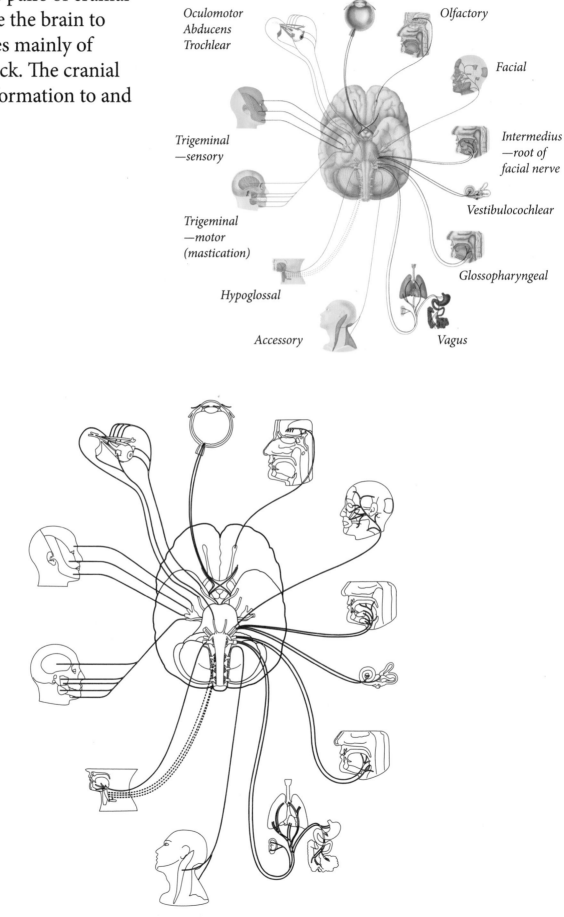

Optic

Oculomotor
Abducens
Trochlear

Olfactory

Facial

Trigeminal
—sensory

Intermedius
—root of
facial nerve

Vestibulocochlear

Trigeminal
—motor
(mastication)

Glossopharyngeal

Hypoglossal

Accessory

Vagus

Olfactory nerves

The olfactory nerves are the tiny sensory nerves of smell. They run from the nasal mucosa to the olfactory bulbs.

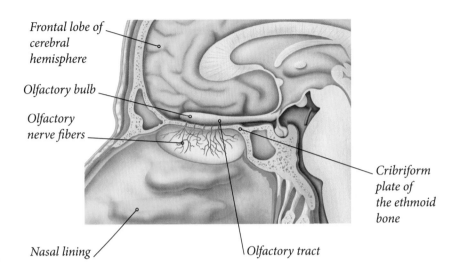

Frontal lobe of cerebral hemisphere

Olfactory bulb

Olfactory nerve fibers

Cribriform plate of the ethmoid bone

Nasal lining

Olfactory tract

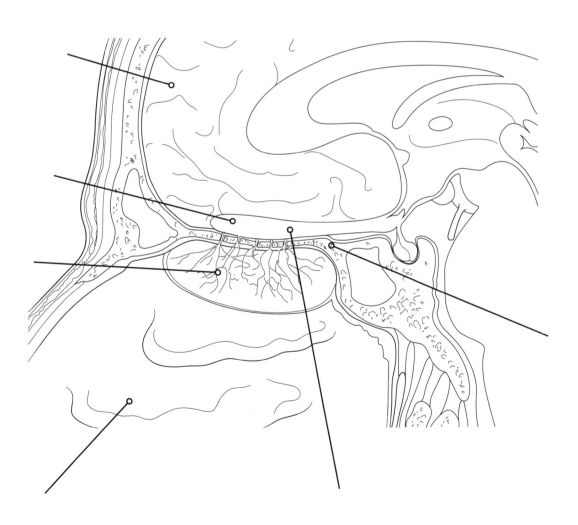

Facial muscles

One of the features that distinguishes humans from animals is our ability to communicate using a wide range of facial expressions. The power behind this ability is a complex system of facial muscles.

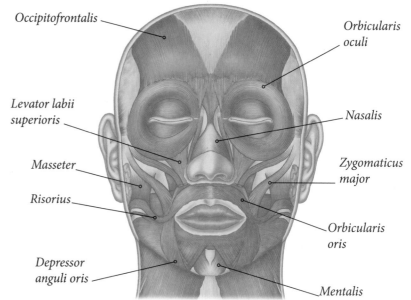

Occipitofrontalis

Orbicularis oculi

Levator labii superioris

Nasalis

Masseter

Zygomaticus major

Risorius

Orbicularis oris

Depressor anguli oris

Mentalis

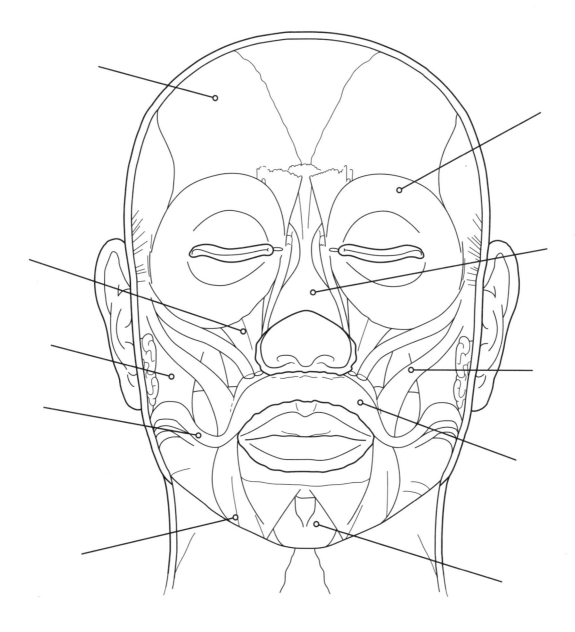

Arteries of the face and neck

The pulse you feel in your neck is blood being pumped to the head via the carotid artery.

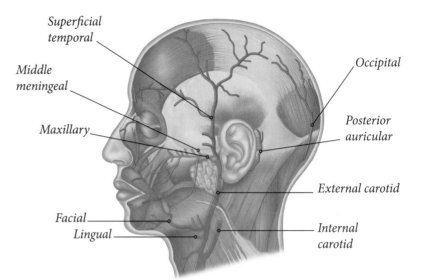

Superficial temporal

Middle meningeal

Maxillary

Facial

Lingual

Occipital

Posterior auricular

External carotid

Internal carotid

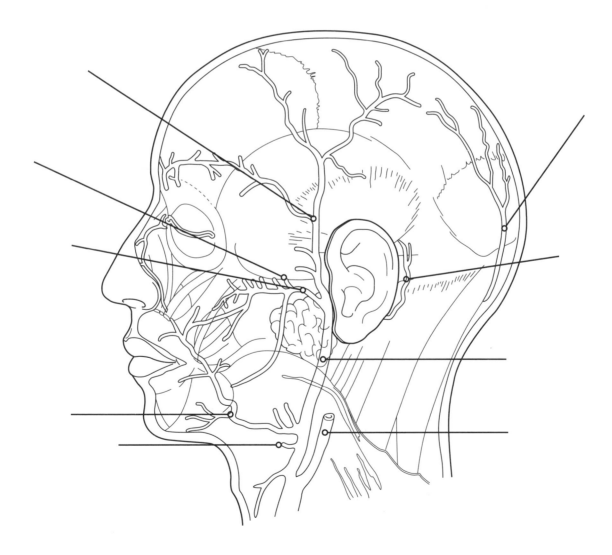

Veins of the face and neck

The veins have a similar distribution around the face and neck as the arteries. Many of the veins also share the same names.

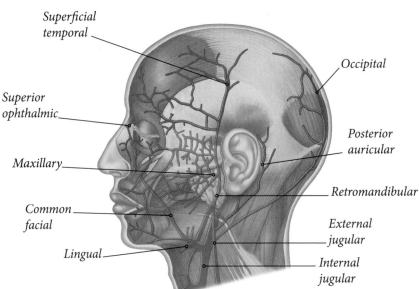

Superficial temporal

Superior ophthalmic

Maxillary

Common facial

Lingual

Occipital

Posterior auricular

Retromandibular

External jugular

Internal jugular

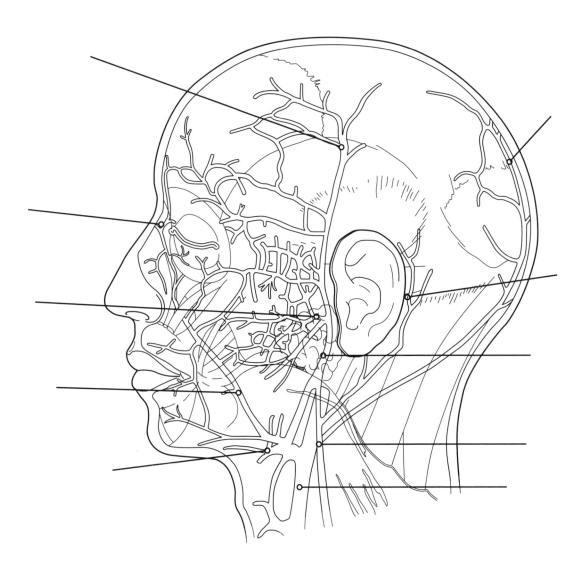

Facial nerves

The facial muscles, and the involuntary functions such as tear formation, are served by the facial nerves, which transmits signals to and from the brain.

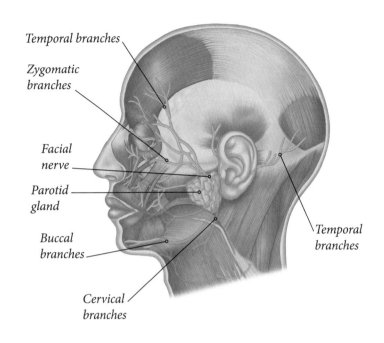

Temporal branches

Zygomatic branches

Facial nerve

Parotid gland

Buccal branches

Cervical branches

Temporal branches

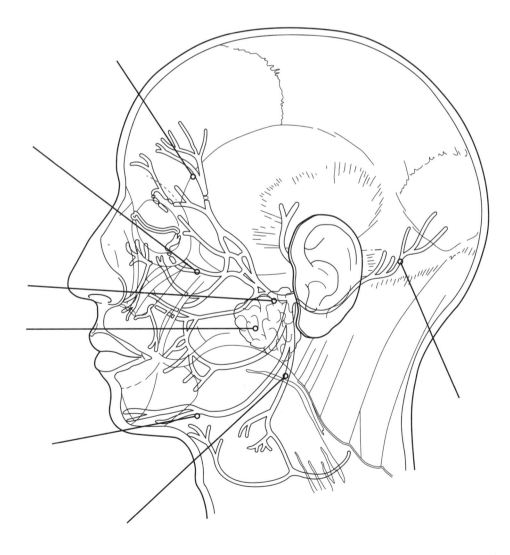

Muscles of mastication

The muscles that help us chew our food also play a part in speech, breathing and yawning.

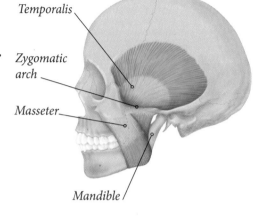

Temporalis

Zygomatic arch

Masseter

Mandible

Lateral pterygoid muscle

Medial pterygoid muscle

Mylohyoid muscle

Hyoid bone

Sternohyoid muscle

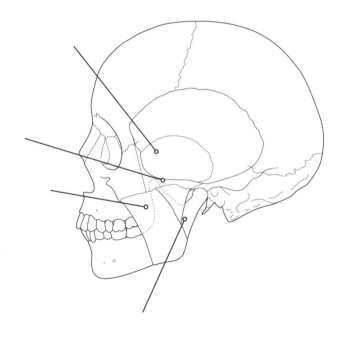

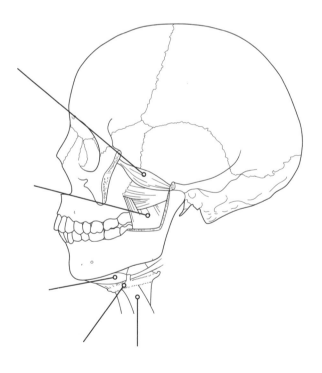

Opening and closing the eye

Whether fluttered alluringly or squeezed tightly shut for protection, the eyelids communicate a range of non-verbal signals. The eyelids are also vital for cleaning and lubricating the eyes.

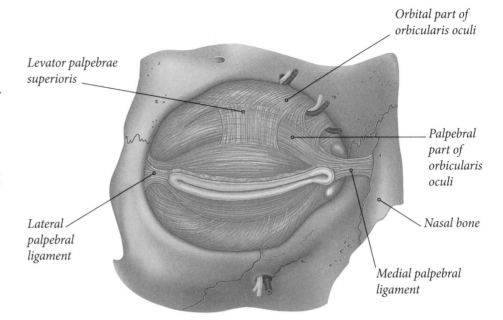

Orbital part of orbicularis oculi

Levator palpebrae superioris

Palpebral part of orbicularis oculi

Nasal bone

Lateral palpebral ligament

Medial palpebral ligament

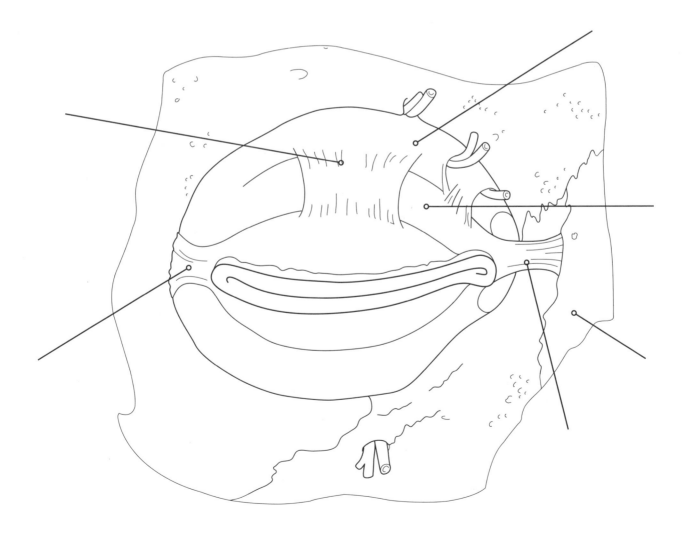

Eyeball

The eyes are the specialized organs of sight, designed to respond to light.

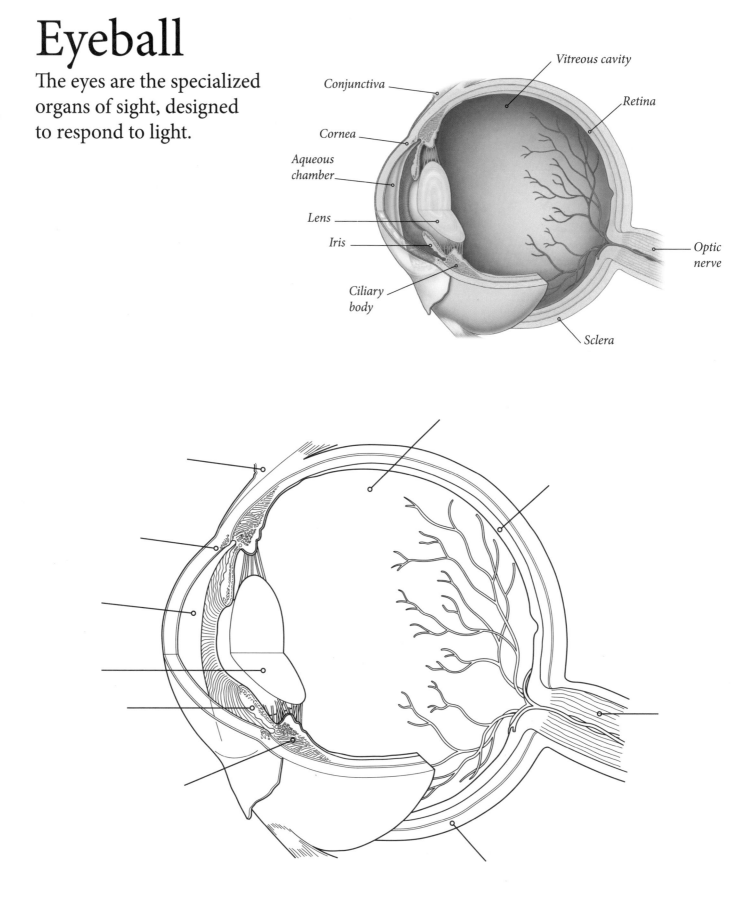

Conjunctiva

Cornea

Aqueous chamber

Lens

Iris

Ciliary body

Vitreous cavity

Retina

Optic nerve

Sclera

Layers of the eye

The eyeball is covered by three different layers, each of which has a special function.

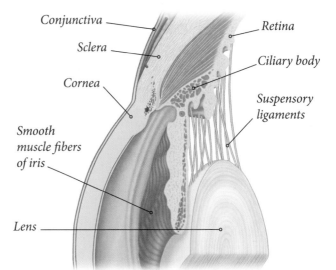

Conjunctiva

Sclera

Cornea

Smooth muscle fibers of iris

Lens

Retina

Ciliary body

Suspensory ligaments

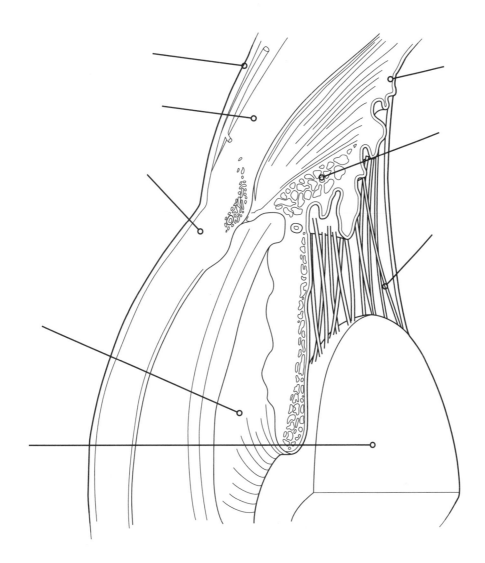

Muscles of the eye

The rotational movements of
the eye are controlled by six
rope-like extra-ocular muscles.

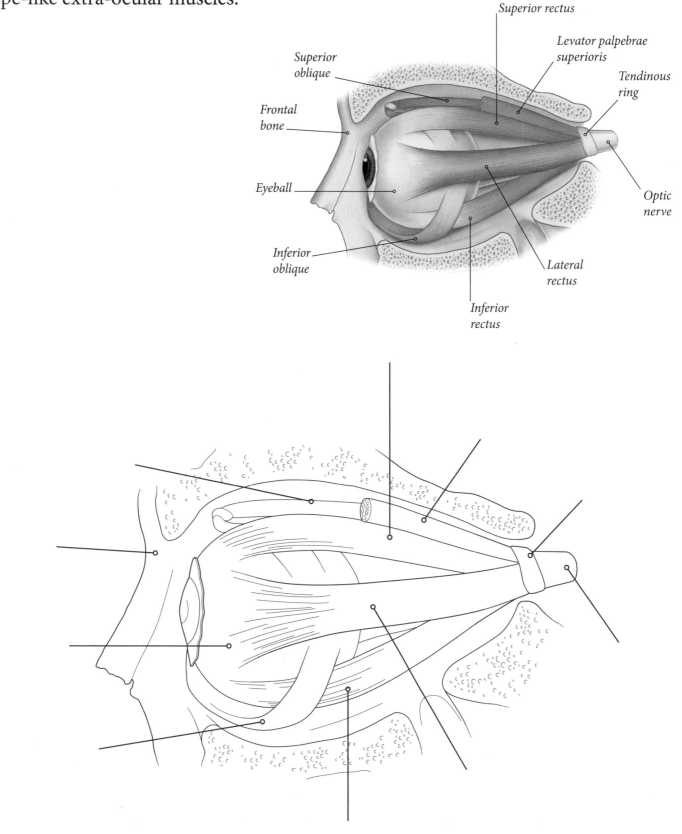

Superior rectus

Levator palpebrae
superioris

Tendinous
ring

Superior
oblique

Frontal
bone

Optic
nerve

Eyeball

Inferior
oblique

Lateral
rectus

Inferior
rectus

Nerves and blood vessels of the eye

The eye muscles are served by a series of nerves and blood vessels that help to make sight our dominant sense.

LEFT EYE FROM ABOVE

Eyeball

Supra-orbital artery

Lacrimal nerve

Ophthalmic artery

Abducens nerve

Oculomotor nerve

Carotid artery

Optic nerve (CNII)

Trigeminal ganglion (CN V)

Abducens nerve (CN VI)

Trochlear nerve (CN IV)

Oculomotor nerve (CN III)

Eyelids

The eyelids are thin folds of skin that can close over the eye to protect it from injury and excessive light.

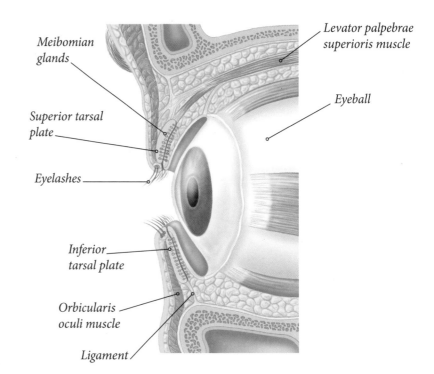

Meibomian glands

Superior tarsal plate

Eyelashes

Inferior tarsal plate

Orbicularis oculi muscle

Ligament

Levator palpebrae superioris muscle

Eyeball

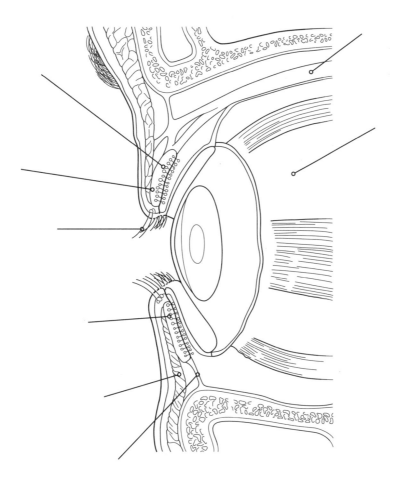

Lacrimal apparatus

The eyes are protected and lubricated by lacrimal fluid, our tears. The lacrimal system produces this fluid and drains the excess to the nasal cavity.

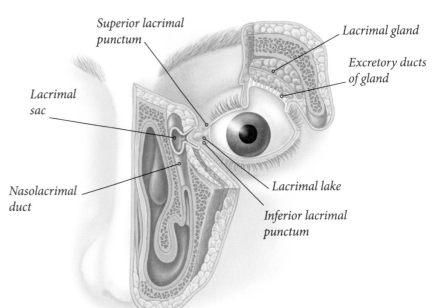

Superior lacrimal punctum

Lacrimal gland

Excretory ducts of gland

Lacrimal sac

Nasolacrimal duct

Lacrimal lake

Inferior lacrimal punctum

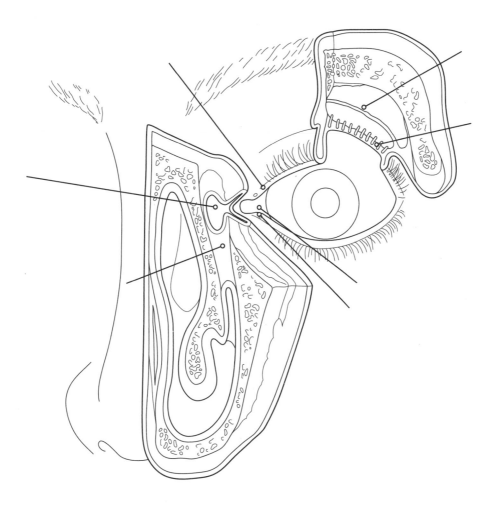

Nose

"Nose" commonly implies just the external structure, but anatomically it also includes the nasal cavity. The nose is the organ of smell and, as the opening of the respiratory tract, it serves to warm and filter air.

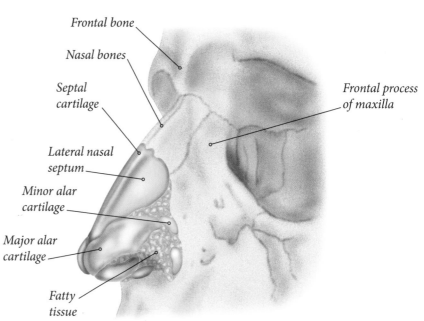

Frontal bone

Nasal bones

Septal cartilage

Lateral nasal septum

Minor alar cartilage

Major alar cartilage

Fatty tissue

Frontal process of maxilla

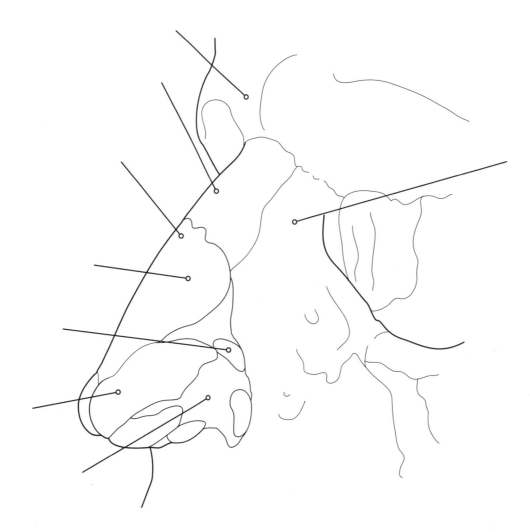

Nasal cavity

The nasal cavity runs from the nostrils to the pharynx, and is divided in two by the septum. The roof forms part of the floor of the cranial cavity.

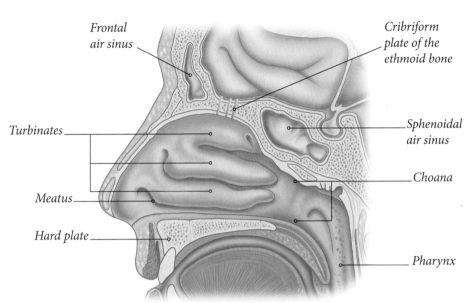

Frontal air sinus

Cribriform plate of the ethmoid bone

Turbinates

Sphenoidal air sinus

Choana

Meatus

Hard plate

Pharynx

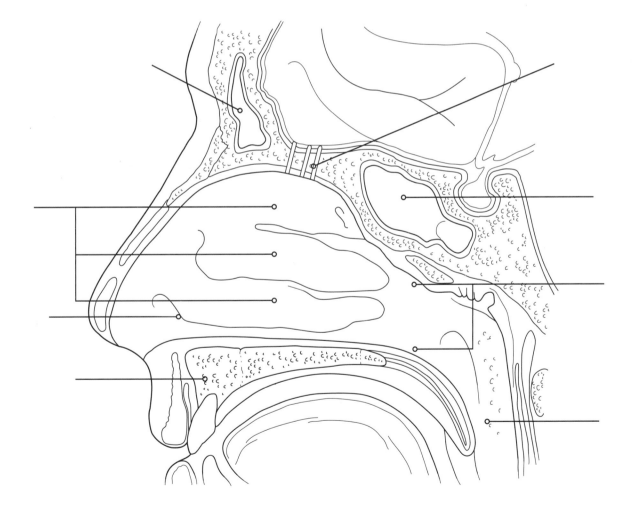

Paranasal sinuses

The term "paranasal" means "by the side of the nose." The paranasal sinuses are air-filled cavities in the bones around the nasal cavity.

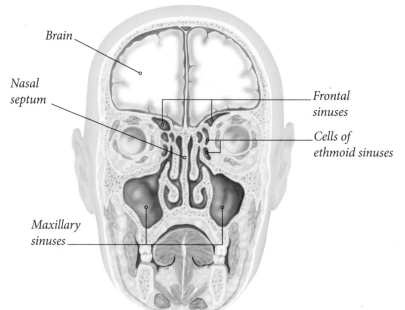

Brain

Nasal septum

Frontal sinuses

Cells of ethmoid sinuses

Maxillary sinuses

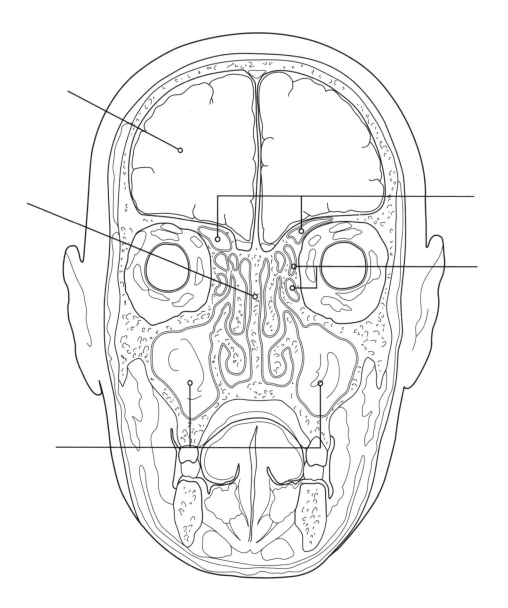

Inside the sinuses

The efficiency of mucous drainage from each of the pairs of sinuses depends on their location. Effective drainage lessens the risk of sinus infection.

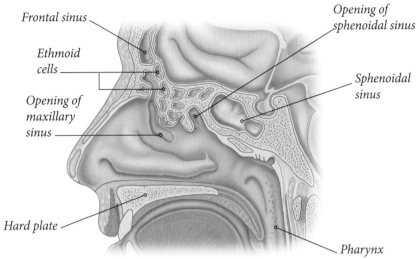

Frontal sinus

Ethmoid cells

Opening of maxillary sinus

Hard plate

Opening of sphenoidal sinus

Sphenoidal sinus

Pharynx

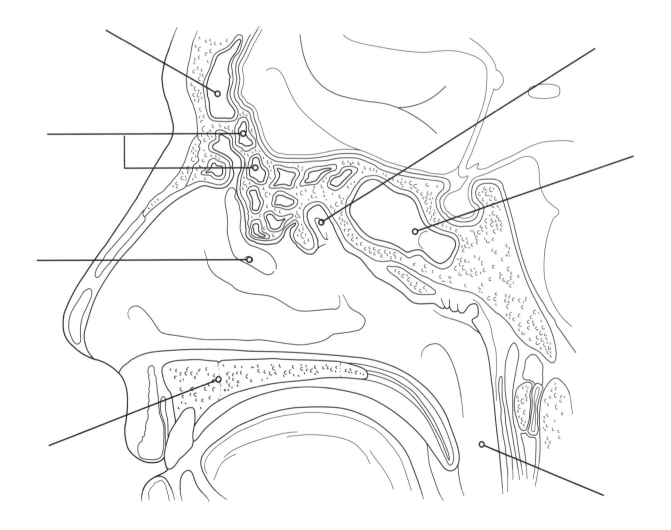

Oral cavity

Also known as the mouth, the oral cavity extends from the lips to the fauces, the opening leading to the pharynx.

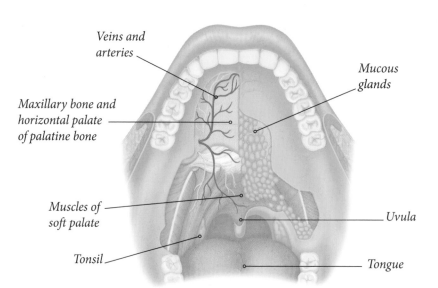

Veins and arteries

Maxillary bone and horizontal palate of palatine bone

Muscles of soft palate

Tonsil

Mucous glands

Uvula

Tongue

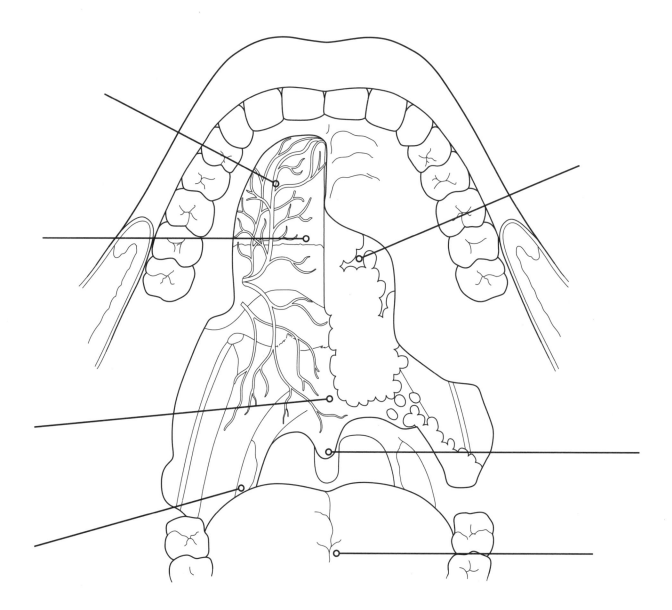

Floor of the mouth

The floor of the mouth acts as the foundation for a network of muscles and glands that are essential to its function.

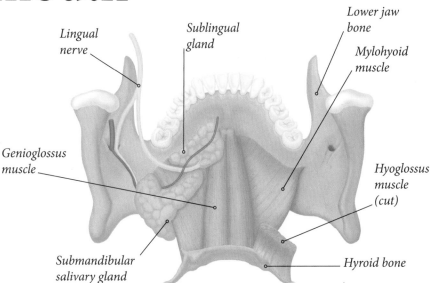

Lingual nerve

Sublingual gland

Lower jaw bone

Mylohyoid muscle

Genioglossus muscle

Hyoglossus muscle (cut)

Submandibular salivary gland

Hyroid bone

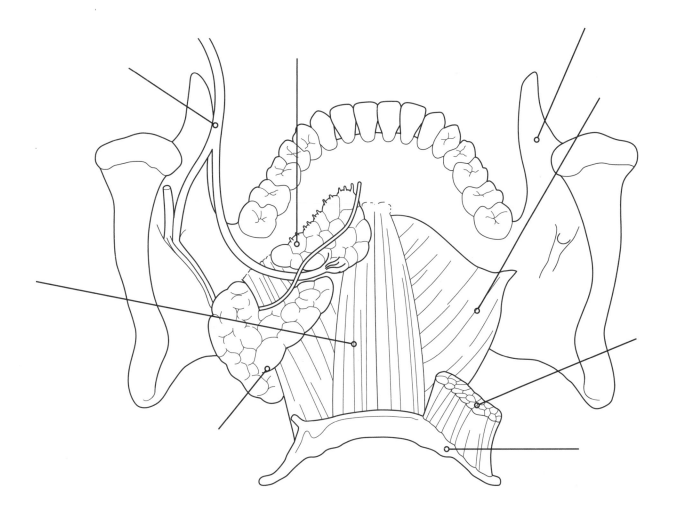

Teeth

Teeth are designed for biting and chewing up food, and each has a particular function.

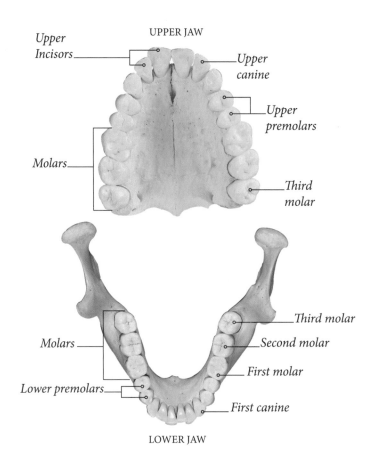

UPPER JAW

Upper Incisors

Upper canine

Upper premolars

Molars

Third molar

Third molar

Second molar

First molar

First canine

Molars

Lower premolars

LOWER JAW

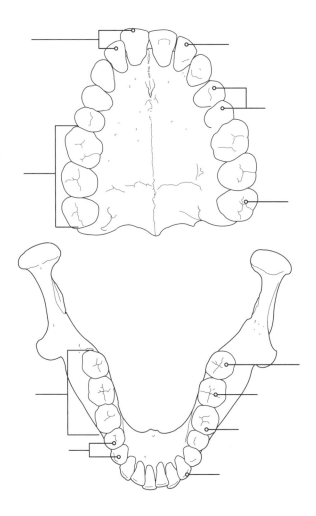

Development of the teeth

There are two major phases
of tooth development during
childhood. This is to allow
the head to grow and adult
teeth to develop.

JAWS OF A
NEWBORN

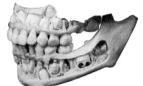

JAWS OF A
SIX-YEAR-OLD

ADULT
MANDIBLE

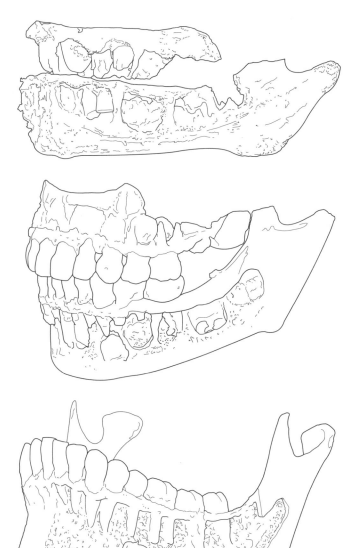

Tongue

The tongue is basically a mass of muscle, whose complex movement is essential for speech, mastication, and swallowing. Its upper surface is lined with specialized tissue that contains taste buds.

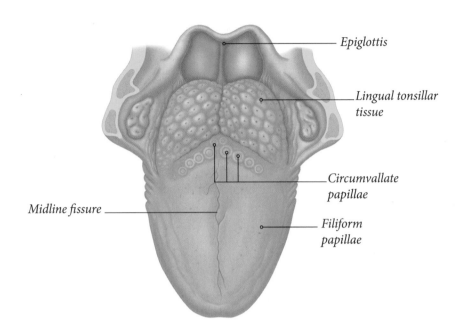

Epiglottis

Lingual tonsillar tissue

Circumvallate papillae

Midline fissure

Filiform papillae

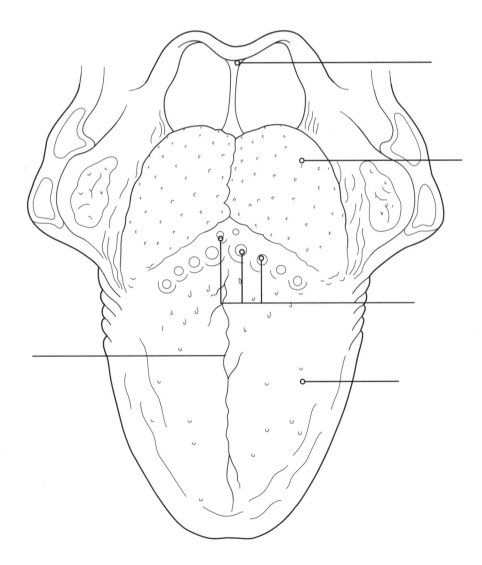

Muscles of the tongue

The muscles within the tongue (intrinsic muscles) comprise three groups of fiber bundles running the length, breadth, and depth of the organ.

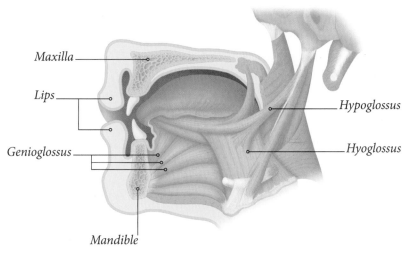

Maxilla

Lips

Genioglossus

Mandible

Hypoglossus

Hyoglossus

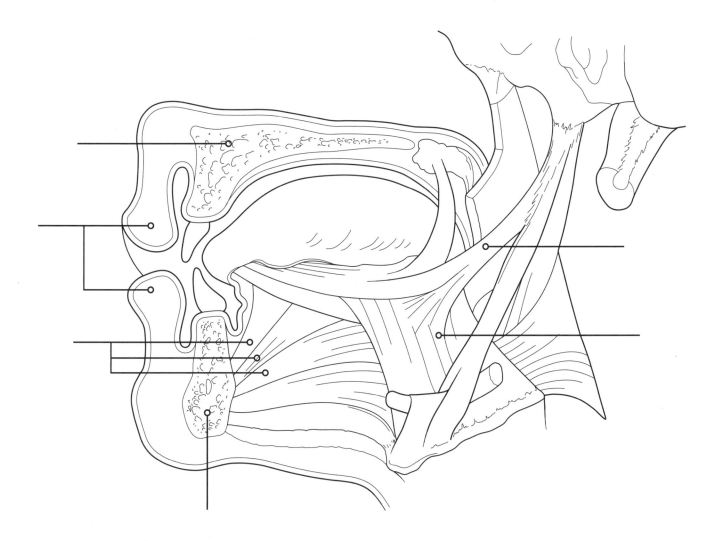

Salivary glands

The salivary glands produce about three-quarters of a liter of saliva a day. Saliva plays a major role in lubricating and protecting the mouth and teeth, as well as aiding swallowing and mastication.

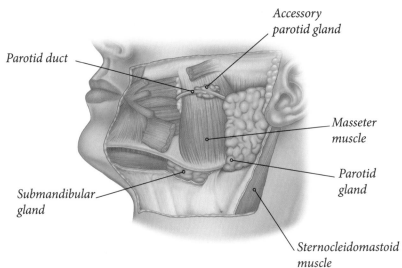

Parotid duct

Accessory parotid gland

Masseter muscle

Parotid gland

Submandibular gland

Sternocleidomastoid muscle

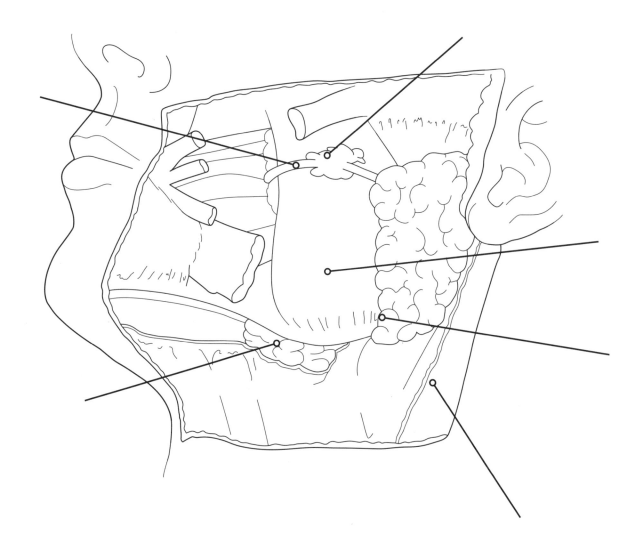

Submandibular and sublingual glands

The two smaller pairs of salivary glands are the submandibular and the sublingual glands situated in the floor of the mouth.

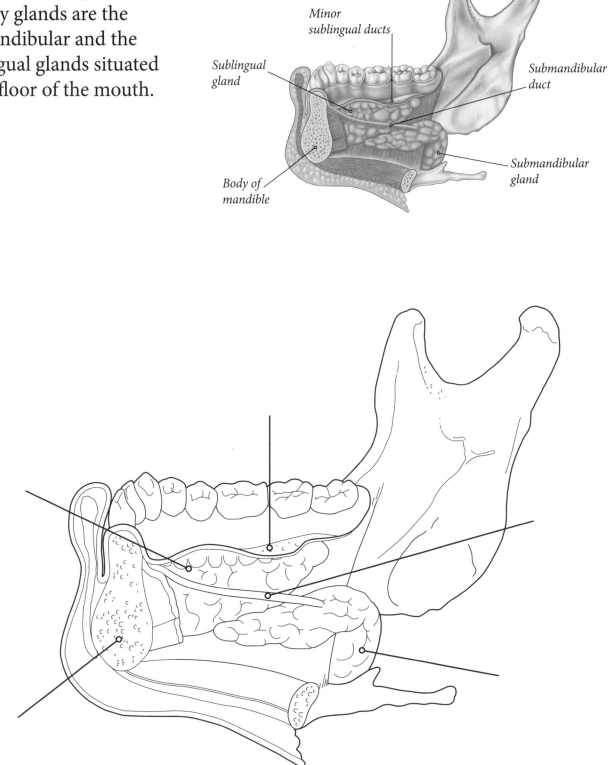

Minor sublingual ducts

Sublingual gland

Submandibular duct

Submandibular gland

Body of mandible

Infratemporal fossa

The infratemporal fossa (a fossa is a depression or hollow) is a region at the side of the head which contains a number of important nerves, blood vessels and muscles involved in mastication (chewing).

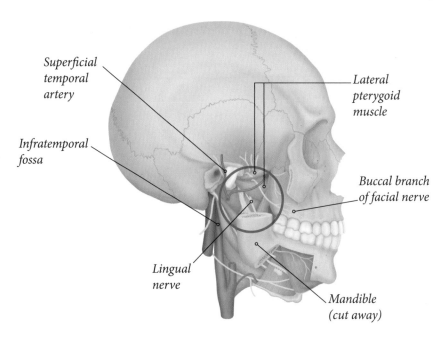

Superficial temporal artery

Infratemporal fossa

Lateral pterygoid muscle

Buccal branch of facial nerve

Lingual nerve

Mandible (cut away)

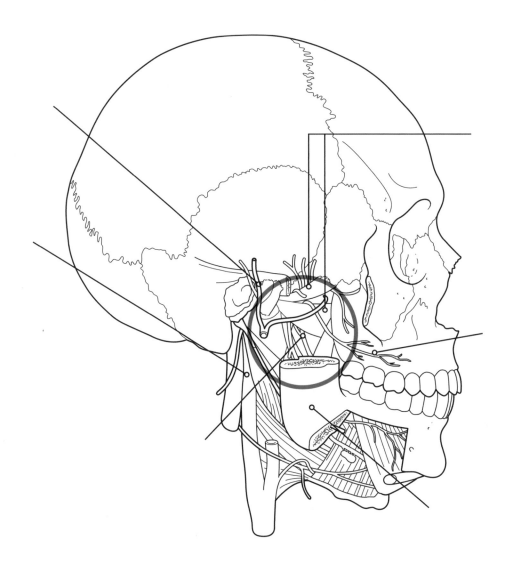

Mandibular nerve

The mandibular nerve leaves the skull (through the foramen ovale) to enter directly into the infratemporal fossa, where it divides into its many branches.

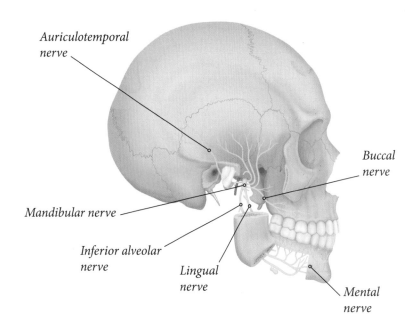

Auriculotemporal nerve

Buccal nerve

Mandibular nerve

Inferior alveolar nerve

Lingual nerve

Mental nerve

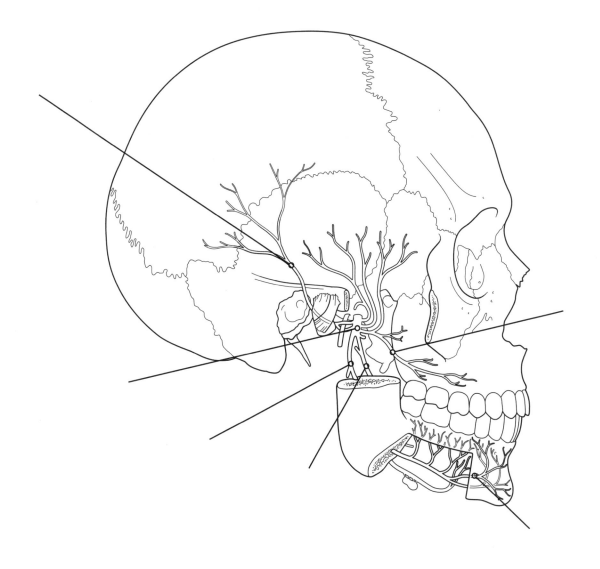

Pterygopalatine fossa

The pterygopalatine fossa is a funnel-shaped space between the bones of the head. It contains important nerves and blood vessels that supply the eye, mouth, nose and face.

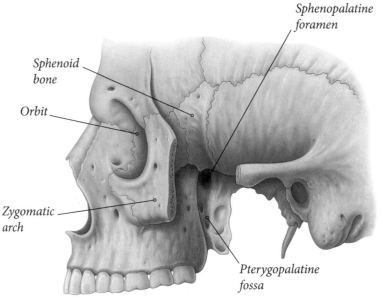

Sphenopalatine foramen

Sphenoid bone

Orbit

Zygomatic arch

Pterygopalatine fossa

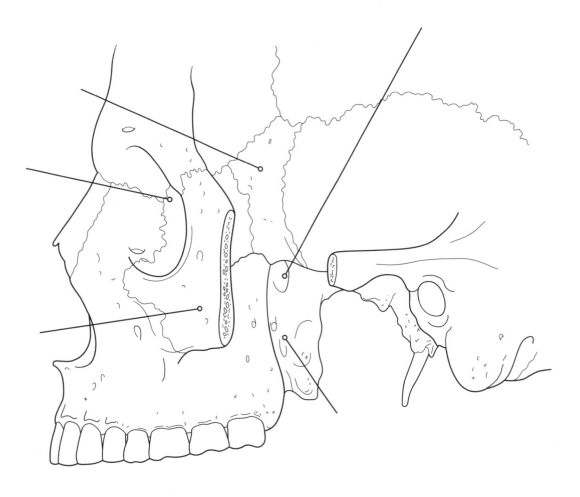

Maxillary nerve

The maxillary nerve enters the pterygopalatine fossa before dividing into branches which supply sensation to large areas of the face.

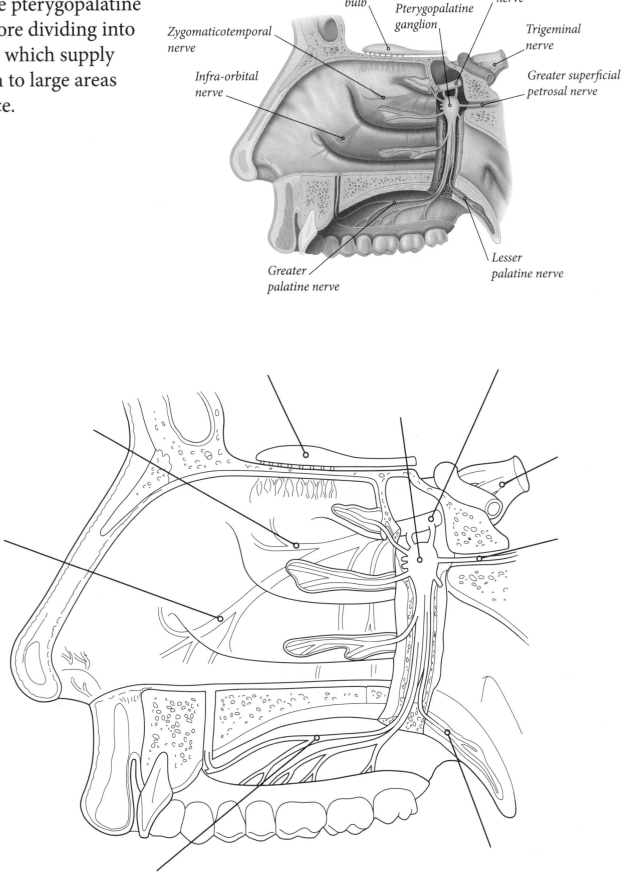

Zygomaticotemporal nerve

Infra-orbital nerve

Olfactory bulb

Pterygopalatine ganglion

Maxillary nerve

Trigeminal nerve

Greater superficial petrosal nerve

Greater palatine nerve

Lesser palatine nerve

Ear

The ears are vital sensory organs of hearing and balance. Each ear is divided into three parts—outer, middle, and inner ear—each of which is designed to respond to sound or movement in a different way.

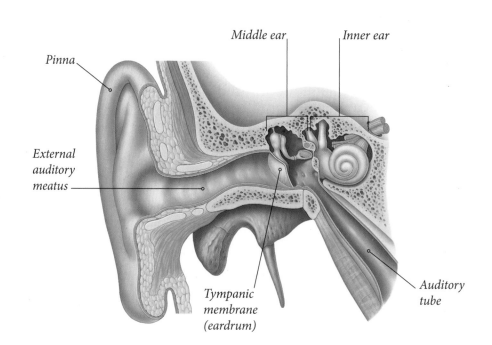

Pinna

Middle ear

Inner ear

External auditory meatus

Tympanic membrane (eardrum)

Auditory tube

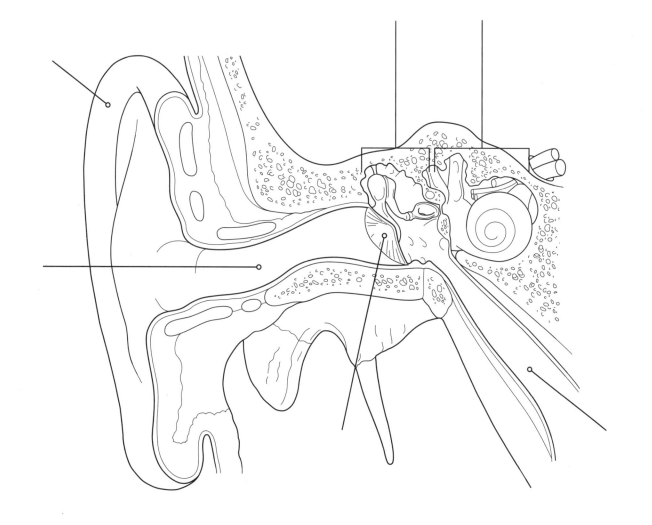

Inside the ear

The middle ear is an air-filled cavity that contains the eardrum and three small bones that help transmit sound to the inner ear. It is also connected to the throat via the auditory tube.

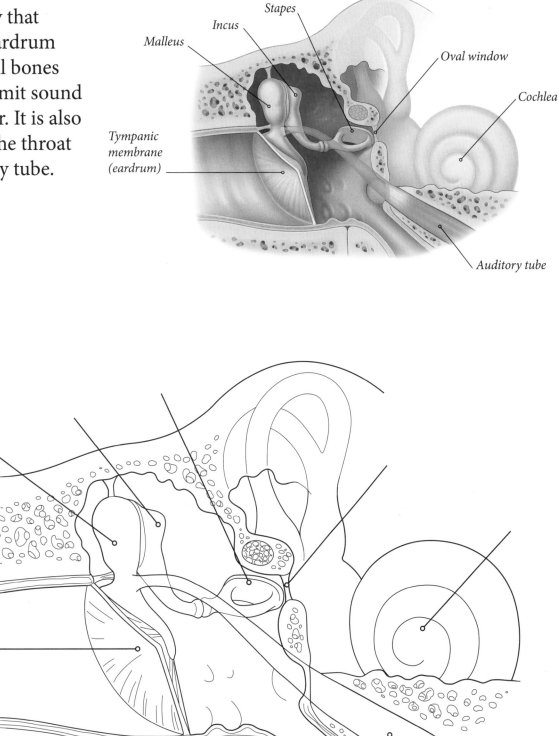

Malleus

Incus

Stapes

Oval window

Cochlea

Tympanic membrane (eardrum)

Auditory tube

Inside the neck

The neck is one of the most anatomically complex areas of the body. Many vital structures, including the spinal cord and thyroid gland, are closely packed together within layers of connecting tissue and muscle.

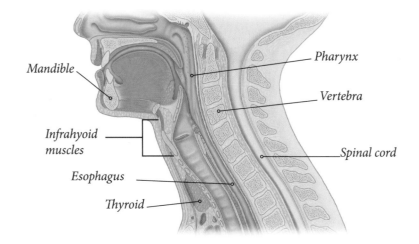

Mandible

Infrahyoid muscles

Esophagus

Thyroid

Pharynx

Vertebra

Spinal cord

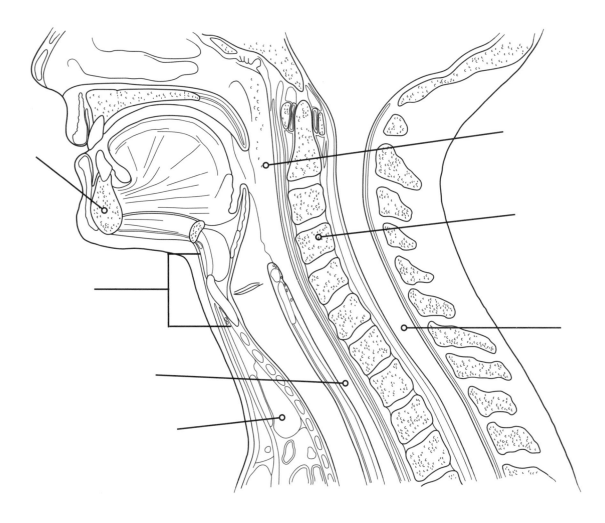

Cross section of the neck

Deeper layers of the neck reveal interconnected sheets of tissue. These bind to and protect a variety of structures.

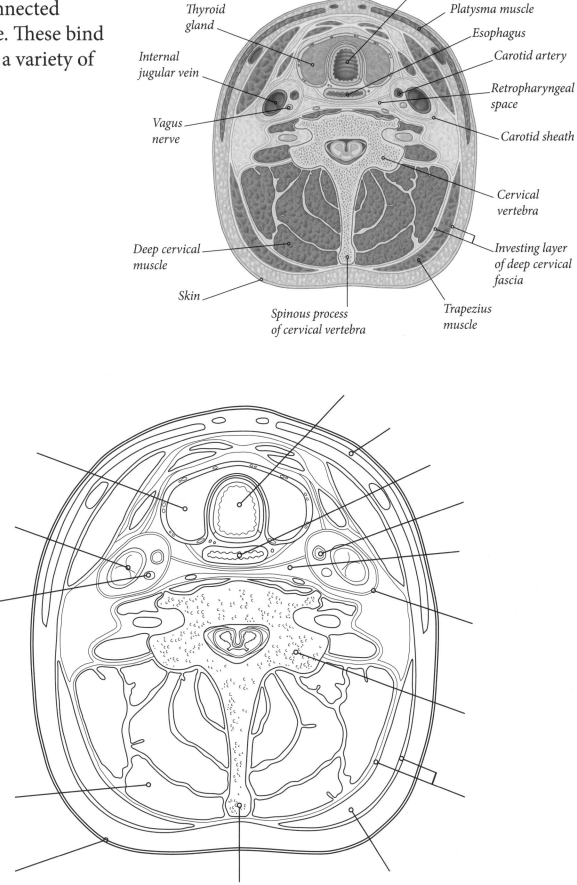

Thyroid gland

Trachea

Platysma muscle

Esophagus

Carotid artery

Retropharyngeal space

Carotid sheath

Cervical vertebra

Investing layer of deep cervical fascia

Trapezius muscle

Spinous process of cervical vertebra

Skin

Deep cervical muscle

Vagus nerve

Internal jugular vein

Vertebral column

The vertebral column gives our bodies flexibility and keeps us upright. It also protects the delicate spinal cord.

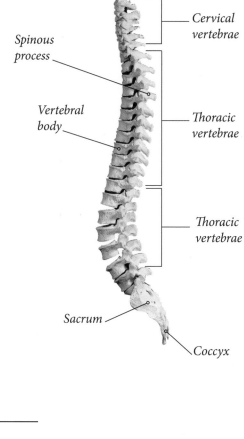

Spinous process

Vertebral body

Cervical vertebrae

Thoracic vertebrae

Thoracic vertebrae

Sacrum

Coccyx

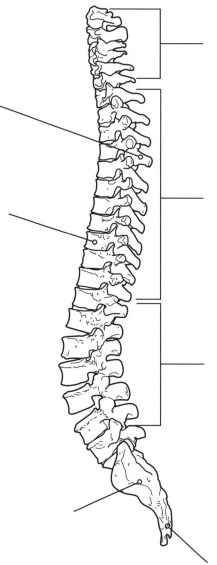

Vertebral connections

The spinal column is divided into five main sections. Each section has a specific function and together they maintain the stability of the skeleton as a whole.

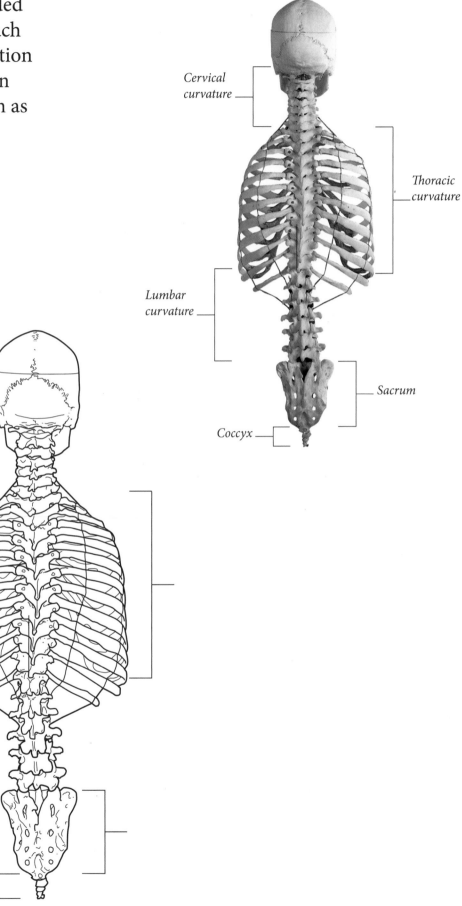

Cervical curvature

Thoracic curvature

Lumbar curvature

Sacrum

Coccyx

Cervical vertebrae

There are seven cervical vertebrae, which together make up the skeletal structure of the neck. These vertebrae protect the spinal cord, support the skull, and allow a range of movement.

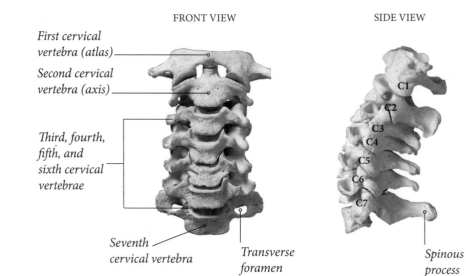

FRONT VIEW

SIDE VIEW

First cervical vertebra (atlas)

Second cervical vertebra (axis)

Third, fourth, fifth, and sixth cervical vertebrae

Seventh cervical vertebra

Transverse foramen

C1
C2
C3
C4
C5
C6
C7

Spinous process

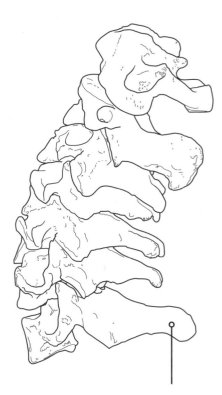

Muscles of the neck

The muscles running up the front of the neck are divided into the suprahyoid and infrahyoid muscle groups. They attach to the hyoid bone and act to raise and lower it and the larynx during swallowing.

Hyoid bone

Mandible

Mylohyoid muscle

Digastric muscle (anterior belly)

Stylohyoid muscle

Digastric muscle (posterior belly)

Thyrohyoid muscle

Internal jugular vein

Omohyoid muscle

Sternothyroid muscle

Sternohyoid muscle

Brainstem

The brainstem lies at the junction of the brain and spinal cord. It helps to regulate breathing and blood circulation as well as having an effect upon a person's level of consciousness.

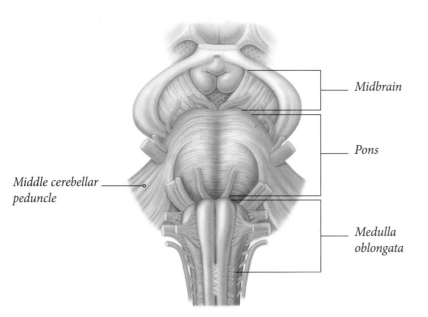

Midbrain

Pons

Middle cerebellar peduncle

Medulla oblongata

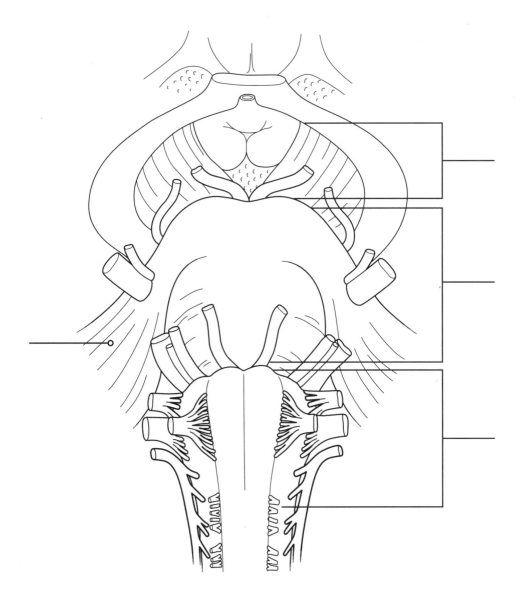

Brachial plexus

Lying within the root of the
neck and extending into the
axilla, the brachial plexus
is a complicated network of
nerves from which
arise the major nerves
supplying the upper limb.

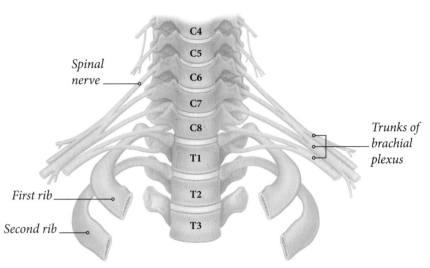

Spinal nerve

Trunks of brachial plexus

First rib

Second rib

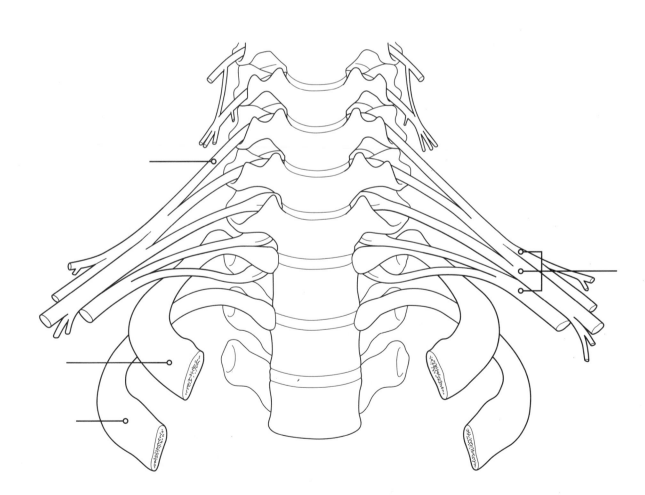

Dermatomes

A dermatome is an area of skin that receives its sensory nerve supply from a single spinal nerve (and therefore a single segment of the spinal cord); however, that nerve supply may actually be taken to the skin in two or more cutaneous branches.

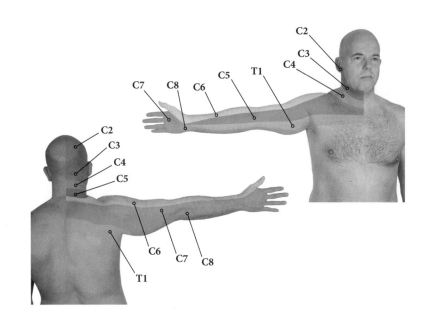

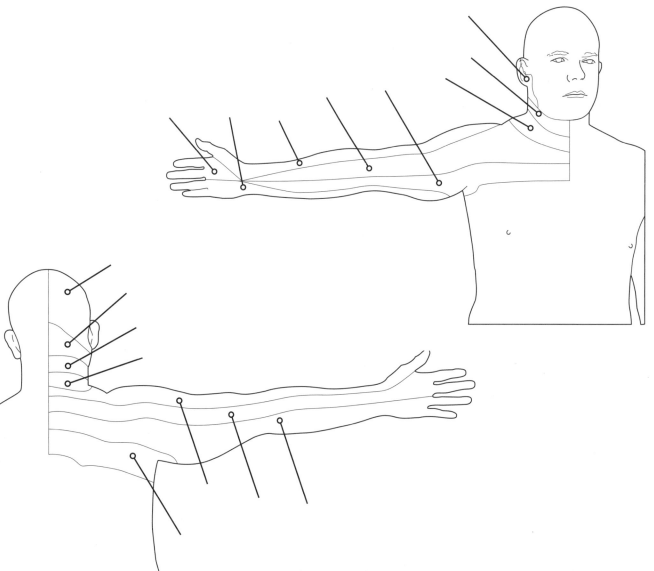

Pharynx

The pharynx, situated at the back of the throat, is a passage both for food to the alimentary system and air to the lungs. It can be divided into three major parts, and the entrance is guarded by the tonsils.

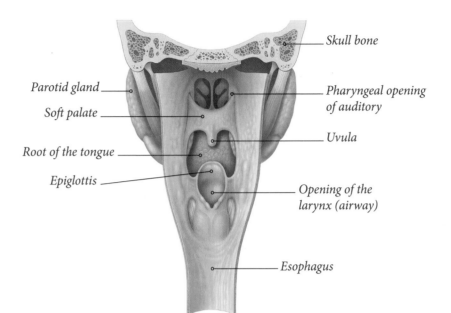

Parotid gland —

Soft palate —

Root of the tongue —

Epiglottis —

Skull bone

Pharyngeal opening of auditory

Uvula

Opening of the larynx (airway)

Esophagus

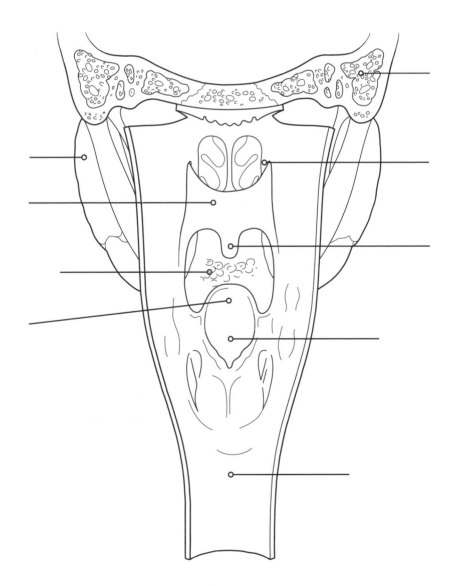

Muscles of the pharynx

There are six pairs of muscles
that make up the pharynx.
These muscles can be divided
into two groups.

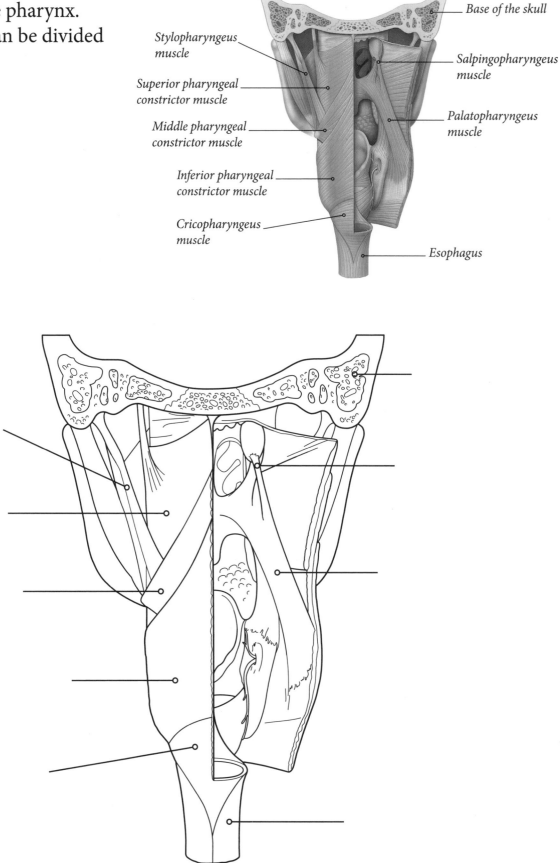

Stylopharyngeus
muscle

Superior pharyngeal
constrictor muscle

Middle pharyngeal
constrictor muscle

Inferior pharyngeal
constrictor muscle

Cricopharyngeus
muscle

Base of the skull

Salpingopharyngeus
muscle

Palatopharyngeus
muscle

Esophagus

Larynx

The larynx is situated in the neck below and in front of the pharynx. It is the inlet protecting the lungs and contains the vocal cords. In men, part of the larynx is visible as the Adam's apple.

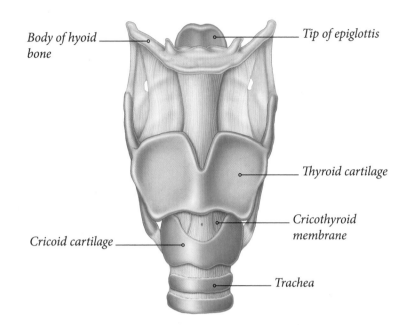

Body of hyoid bone

Tip of epiglottis

Thyroid cartilage

Cricothyroid membrane

Cricoid cartilage

Trachea

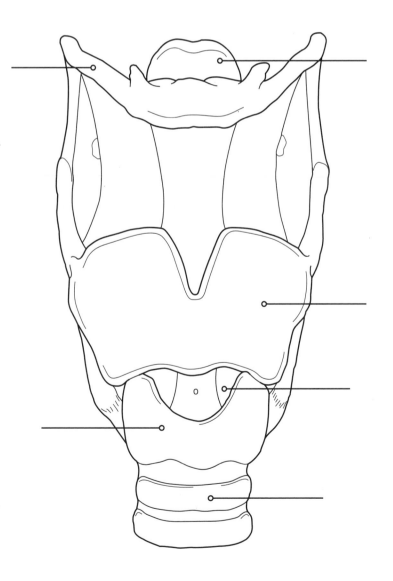

Muscles of the larynx

The muscles of the larynx act to close the laryngeal inlet while swallowing and move the vocal cords to enable vocalization.

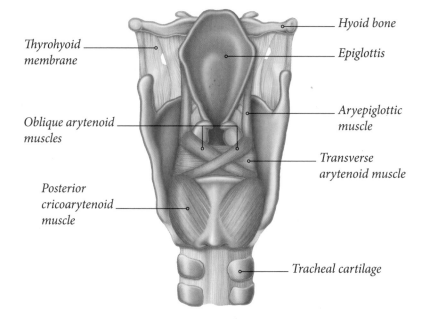

Thyrohyoid membrane

Oblique arytenoid muscles

Posterior cricoarytenoid muscle

Hyoid bone

Epiglottis

Aryepiglottic muscle

Transverse arytenoid muscle

Tracheal cartilage

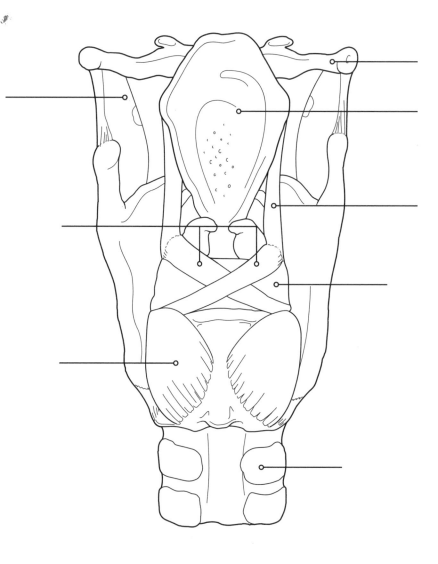

Thyroid and parathyroid glands

The thyroid and parathyroid glands are situated in the neck. Together, they produce important hormones responsible for regulating growth, metabolism, and calcium levels in the blood.

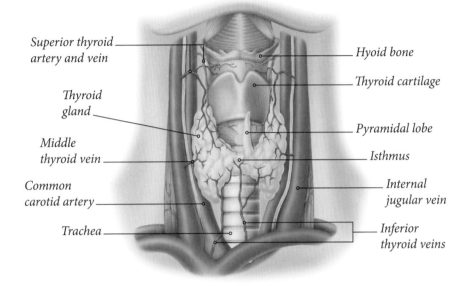

Superior thyroid artery and vein

Thyroid gland

Middle thyroid vein

Common carotid artery

Trachea

Hyoid bone

Thyroid cartilage

Pyramidal lobe

Isthmus

Internal jugular vein

Inferior thyroid veins

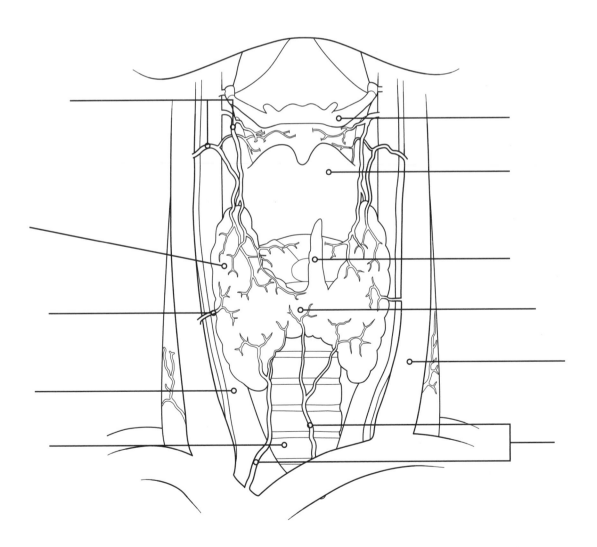

Posterior view of the thyroid

The posterior view of the thyroid reveals the small parathyroid glands, embedded within the lobes. A rich network of vessels supply the glands.

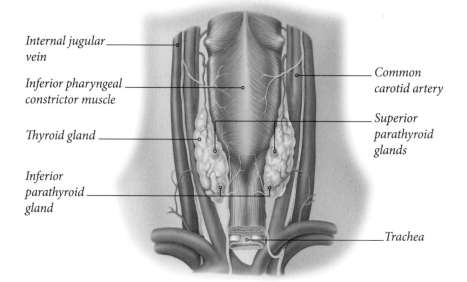

Internal jugular vein

Inferior pharyngeal constrictor muscle

Thyroid gland

Inferior parathyroid gland

Common carotid artery

Superior parathyroid glands

Trachea

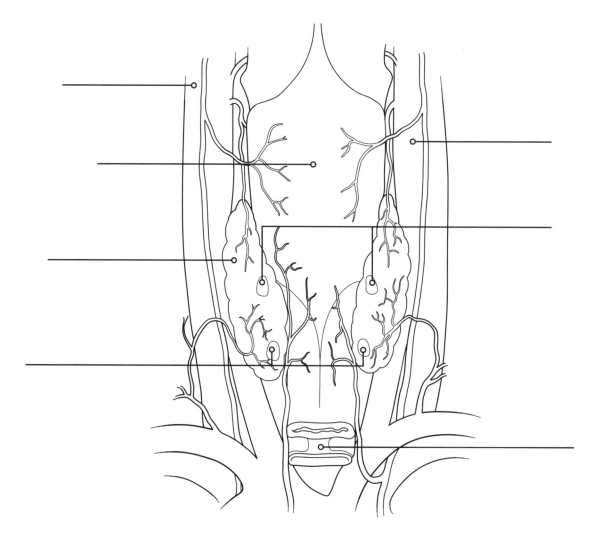

Thoracic vertebrae

The 12 thoracic vertebrae
are the bones of the
spinal column to which
the ribs are attached.
The thoracic vertebrae
sit between the cervical
vertebrae of the neck and
the lumbar vertebrae of
the lower back.

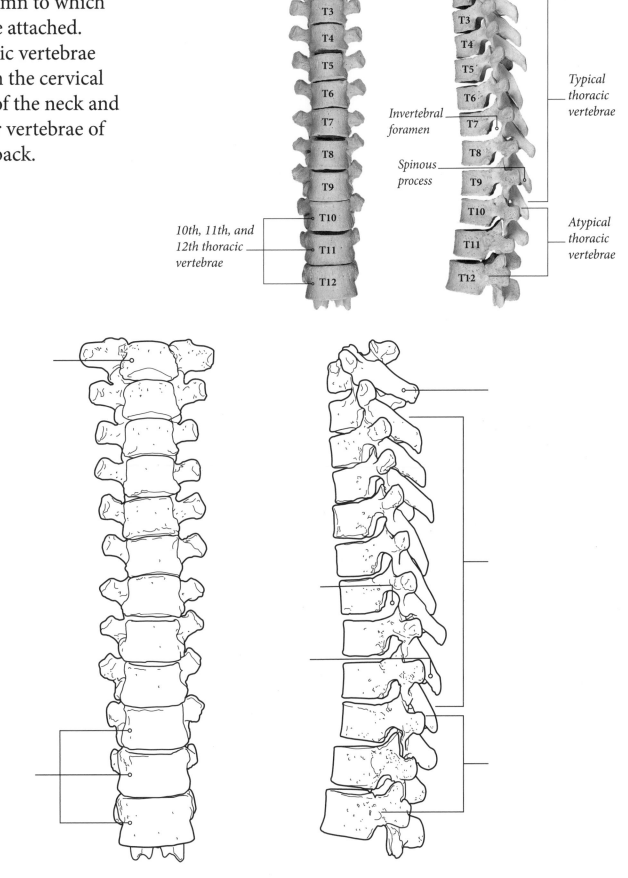

First thoracic
vertebra

T1
T2
T3
T4
T5
T6
T7
T8
T9
T10
T11
T12

10th, 11th, and
12th thoracic
vertebrae

Atypical
thoracic
vertebra

T1
T2
T3
T4
T5
T6
T7
T8
T9
T10
T11
T12

Typical
thoracic
vertebrae

Invertebral
foramen

Spinous
process

Atypical
thoracic
vertebrae

Lumbar vertebrae

The five lumbar vertebrae
of the lower back are the
strongest vertebrae of the
spinal column.

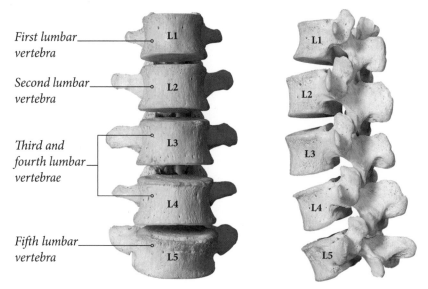

First lumbar vertebra — L1

Second lumbar vertebra — L2

Third and fourth lumbar vertebrae — L3, L4

Fifth lumbar vertebra — L5

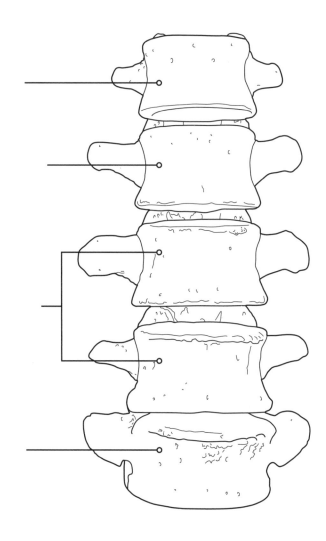

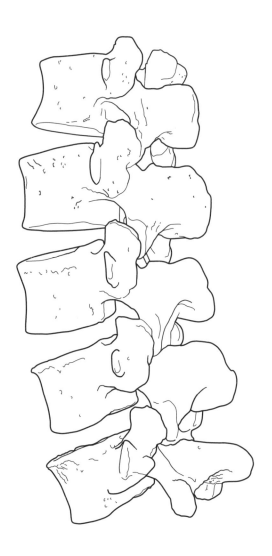

Lumbar ligaments

The intervertebral discs and connecting ligaments support the bones of the spine. They act as shock absorbers, reducing wear on the vertebrae.

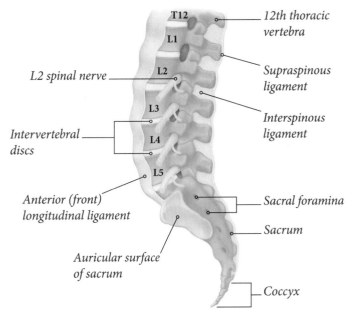

- T12
- L1
- L2
- L3
- L4
- L5

12th thoracic vertebra

Supraspinous ligament

Interspinous ligament

L2 spinal nerve

Intervertebral discs

Anterior (front) longitudinal ligament

Auricular surface of sacrum

Sacral foramina

Sacrum

Coccyx

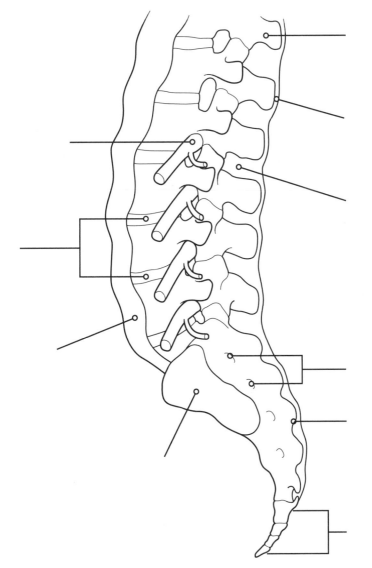

Sacrum and coccyx

The sacrum and coccyx form the tail end of the spinal column. Both are formed from fused vertebrae, allowing attachment for weight-bearing ligaments and muscles, and helping to protect pelvic organs.

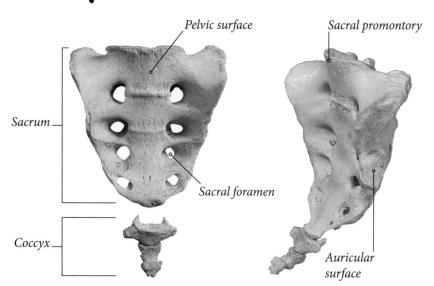

Pelvic surface

Sacral promontory

Sacrum

Sacral foramen

Coccyx

Auricular surface

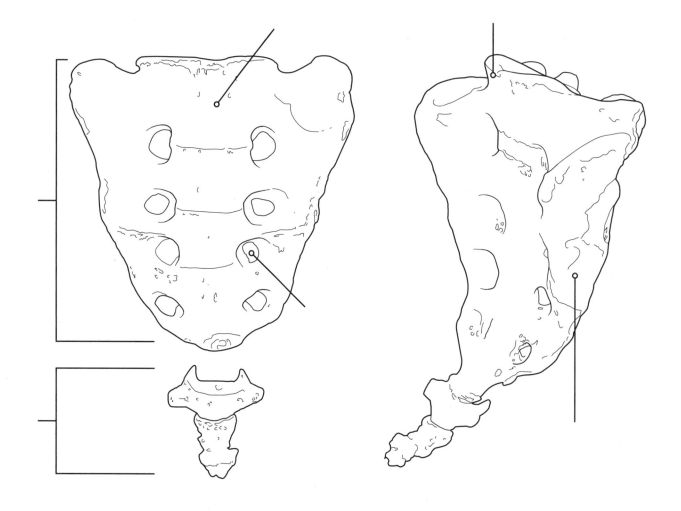

Spinal nerve roots

The genitals, buttocks, and lower
limbs are supplied by nerve roots
that emerge from the lumbar
and sacral spine.

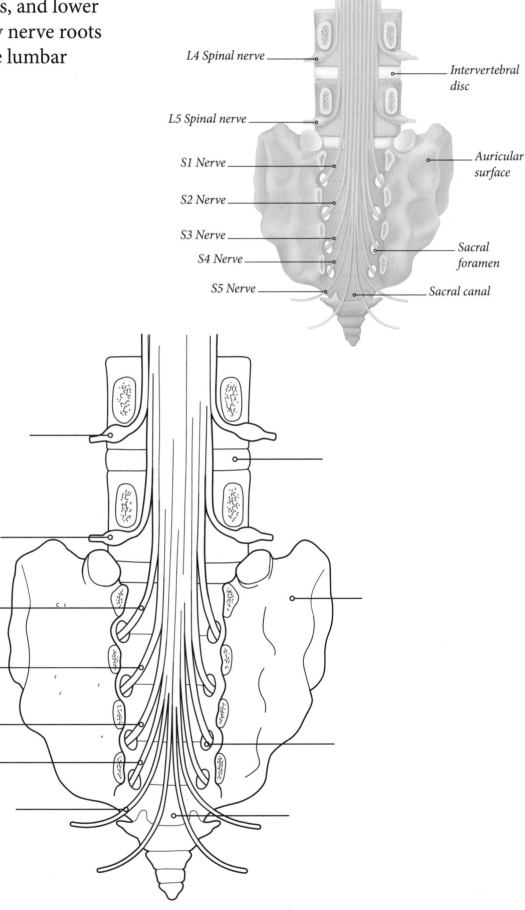

L4 Spinal nerve

Intervertebral
disc

L5 Spinal nerve

S1 Nerve

Auricular
surface

S2 Nerve

S3 Nerve

Sacral
foramen

S4 Nerve

S5 Nerve

Sacral canal

Spinal cord

The spinal cord is the communication pathway between the brain and the body. It allows signals to pass down to control body function and up to inform the brain of what is happening in the body.

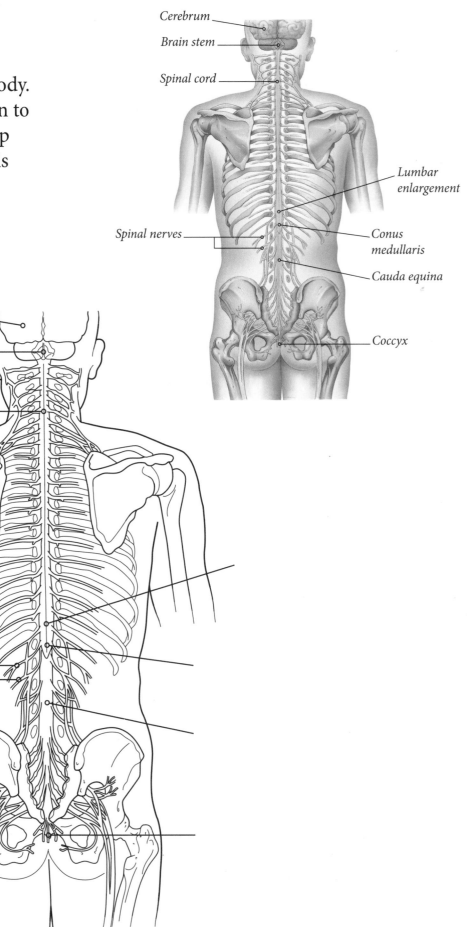

Cerebrum

Brain stem

Spinal cord

Lumbar enlargement

Spinal nerves

Conus medullaris

Cauda equina

Coccyx

Cross section of the spinal cord

The appearance of the spinal cord varies at different levels, according to the amount of muscle supplied by the nerves that emanate from it.

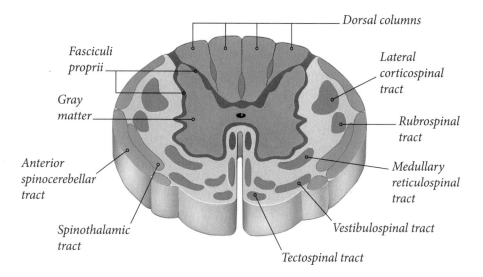

Dorsal columns

Fasciculi proprii

Gray matter

Lateral corticospinal tract

Rubrospinal tract

Medullary reticulospinal tract

Anterior spinocerebellar tract

Spinothalamic tract

Tectospinal tract

Vestibulospinal tract

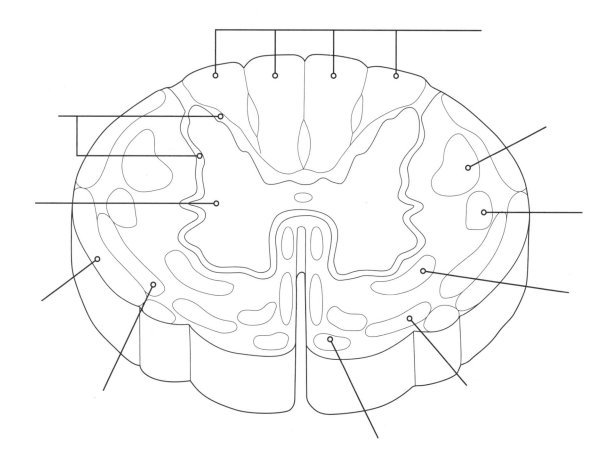

Spinal nerves

There are 31 pairs of spinal nerves, arranged on each side of the spinal cord along its length. The pairs are grouped by region: eight cervical, twelve thoracic, five lumbar, five sacral, and one coccygeal.

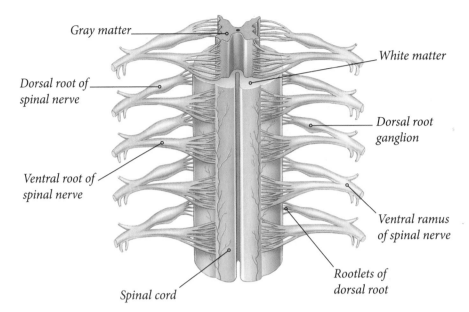

Gray matter

White matter

Dorsal root of spinal nerve

Dorsal root ganglion

Ventral root of spinal nerve

Ventral ramus of spinal nerve

Rootlets of dorsal root

Spinal cord

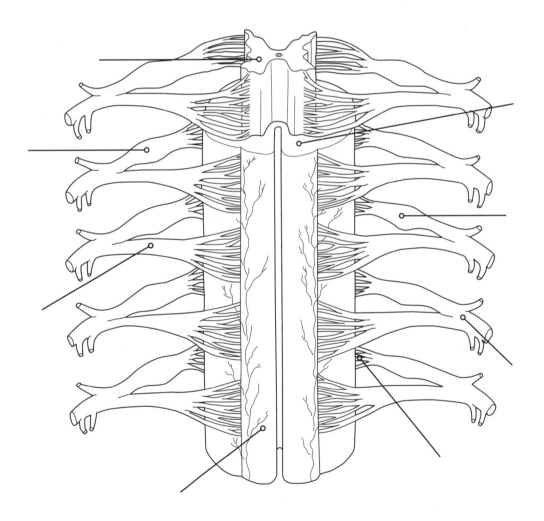

Muscles of the back

The muscles of the back give us our upright posture and allow flexibility and mobility of the spine. The superficial back muscles also act with other muscles to move the shoulders and upper arms.

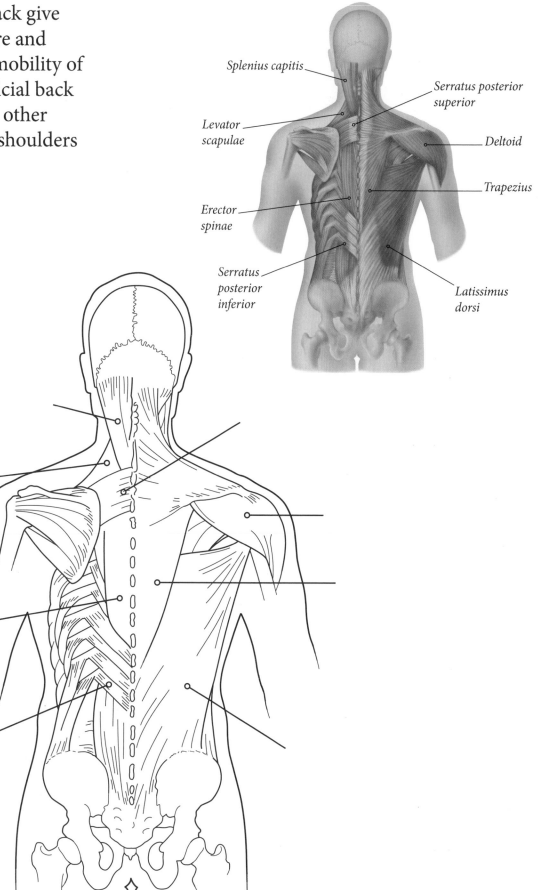

Splenius capitis

Serratus posterior superior

Levator scapulae

Deltoid

Erector spinae

Trapezius

Serratus posterior inferior

Latissimus dorsi

Deep muscles of the back

The deep muscles of the back attach to underlying bones of the spine, pelvis, and ribs. They act together to allow smooth movements of the spine.

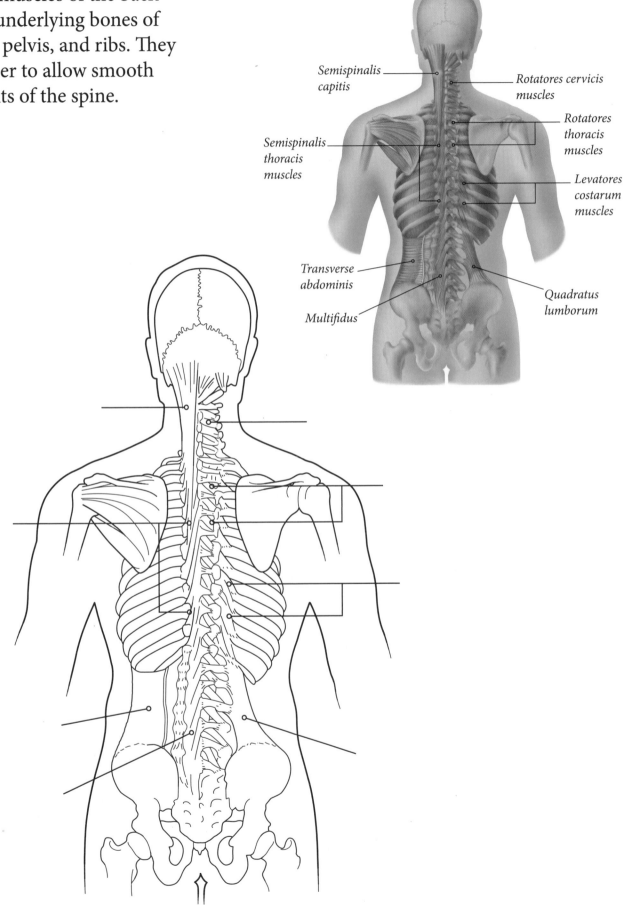

Semispinalis capitis

Rotatores cervicis muscles

Rotatores thoracis muscles

Semispinalis thoracis muscles

Levatores costarum muscles

Transverse abdominis

Quadratus lumborum

Multifidus

Pectoral girdle

The pectoral, or shoulder, girdle is the bony structure that articulates with and supports the upper limbs. It consists of the clavicles at the front of the chest and the scapulae that lie flat against the back.

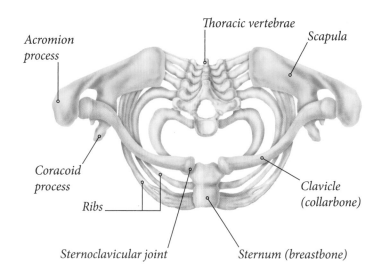

Acromion process

Thoracic vertebrae

Scapula

Coracoid process

Ribs

Clavicle (collarbone)

Sternoclavicular joint

Sternum (breastbone)

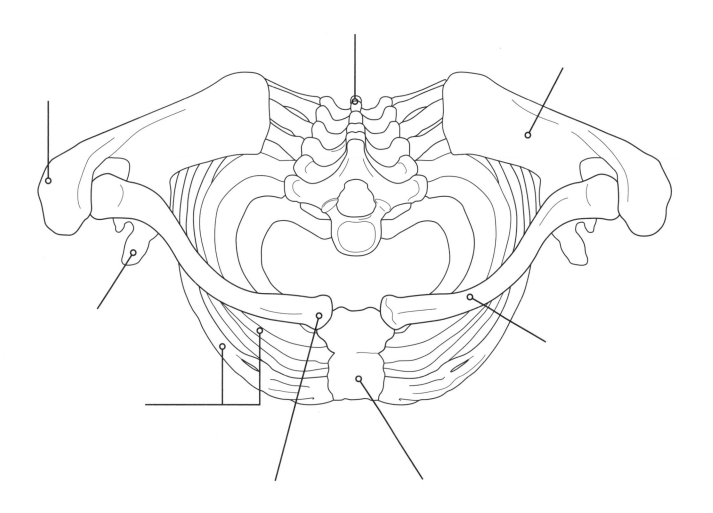

Muscles of the pectoral girdle

The pectoral girdle consists of the scapulae and clavicles, and is responsible for attaching the upper limbs to the central skeleton. The pectoral girdle muscles hold the scapulae and clavicles in place.

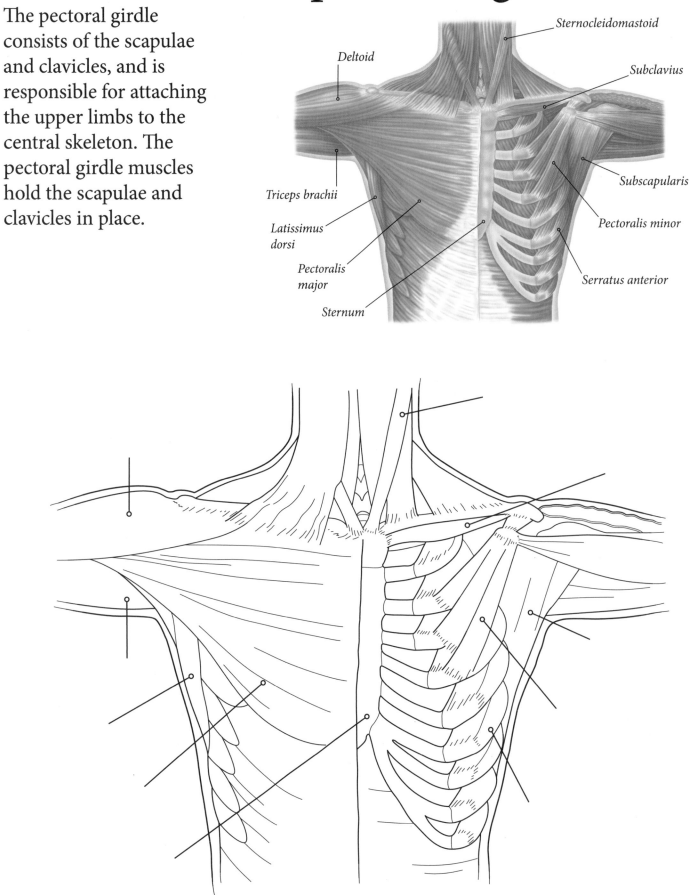

Sternocleidomastoid

Deltoid

Subclavius

Subscapularis

Triceps brachii

Latissimus dorsi

Pectoralis minor

Pectoralis major

Serratus anterior

Sternum

Pectoral girdle from the back

The large trapezius and latissimus dorsi are superficial muscles of the back that attach to and influence the movement of the pectoral girdle.

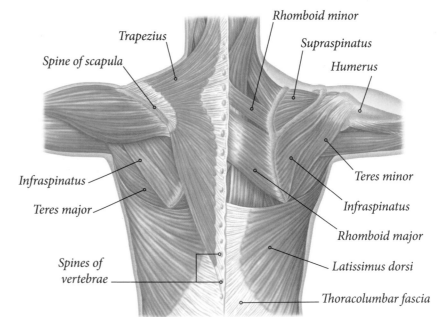

Trapezius

Spine of scapula

Rhomboid minor

Supraspinatus

Humerus

Infraspinatus

Teres major

Teres minor

Infraspinatus

Rhomboid major

Latissimus dorsi

Spines of vertebrae

Thoracolumbar fascia

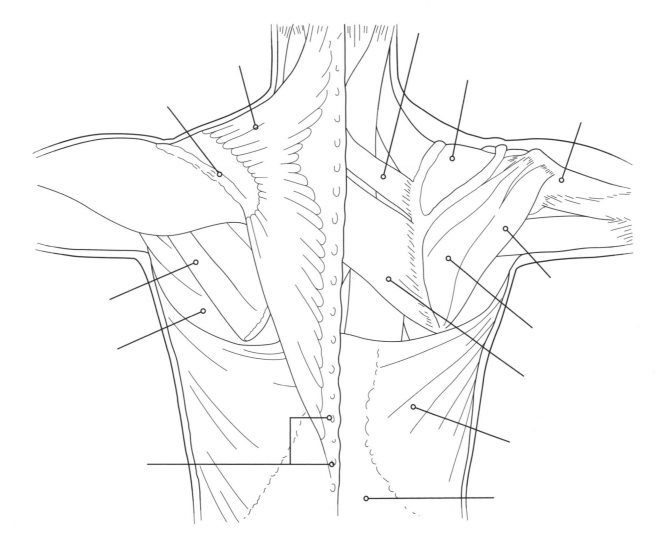

Ribcage

The ribcage protects the vital organs of the thorax, as well as providing sites for the attachment of muscles of the back, chest, and shoulders. It is also light enough to move during breathing.

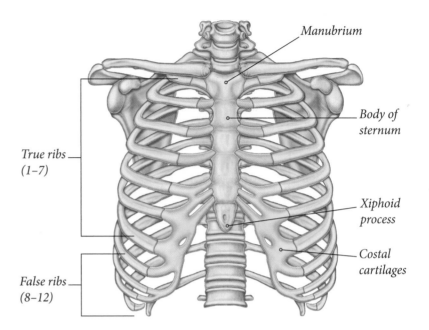

Manubrium

Body of sternum

True ribs (1–7)

Xiphoid process

Costal cartilages

False ribs (8–12)

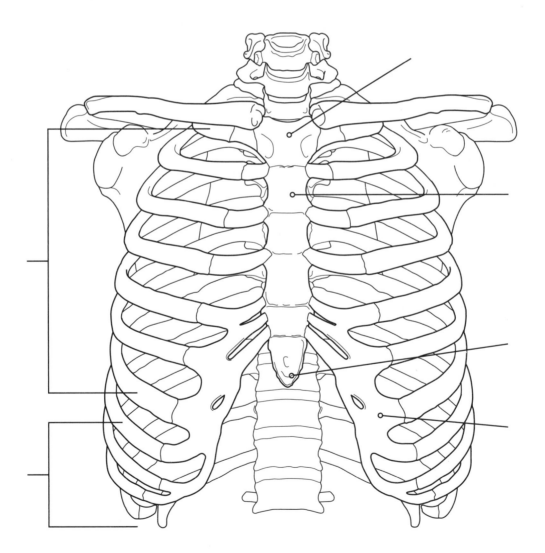

Sternum

The sternum (breastbone) is a long, flat bone that lies vertically at the center of the anterior (front) surface of the ribcage.

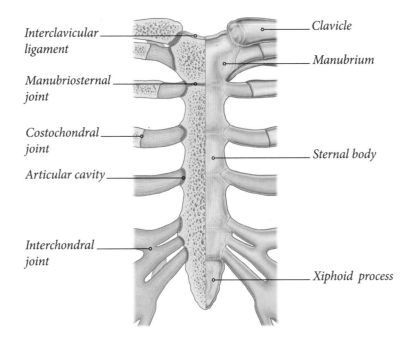

Interclavicular ligament

Clavicle

Manubrium

Manubriosternal joint

Costochondral joint

Sternal body

Articular cavity

Interchondral joint

Xiphoid process

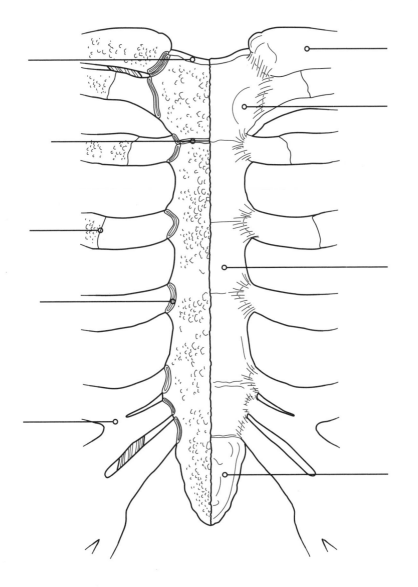

Muscles of the ribcage

The bony skeleton of the ribcage is sheathed in several layers of muscle that include many of the powerful muscles of the upper limbs and back, as well as those that act upon the ribcage alone.

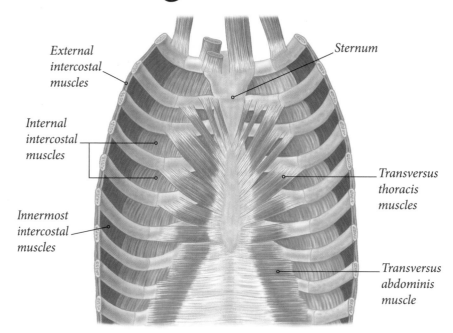

External intercostal muscles

Internal intercostal muscles

Innermost intercostal muscles

Sternum

Transversus thoracis muscles

Transversus abdominis muscle

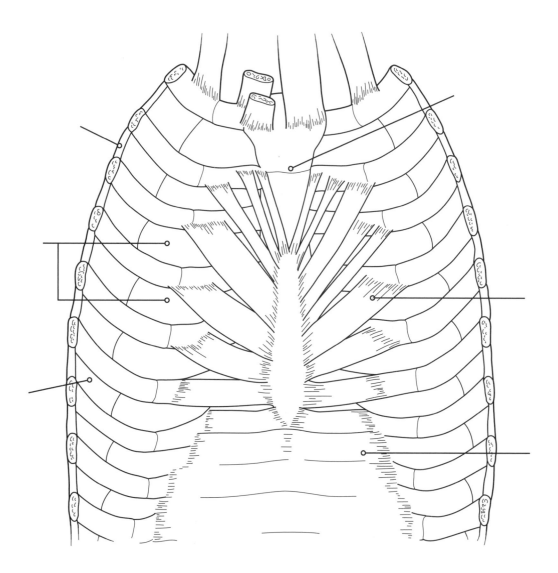

Female breast

The breast undergoes structural changes throughout the life of a woman. The most obvious changes occur during pregnancy as the breast prepares for its function as the source of milk for the baby.

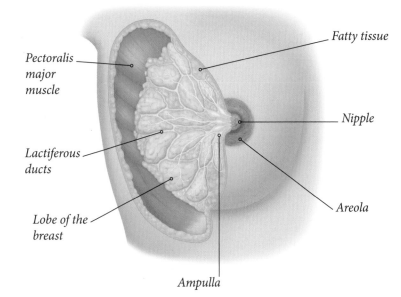

Pectoralis major muscle

Fatty tissue

Lactiferous ducts

Nipple

Lobe of the breast

Areola

Ampulla

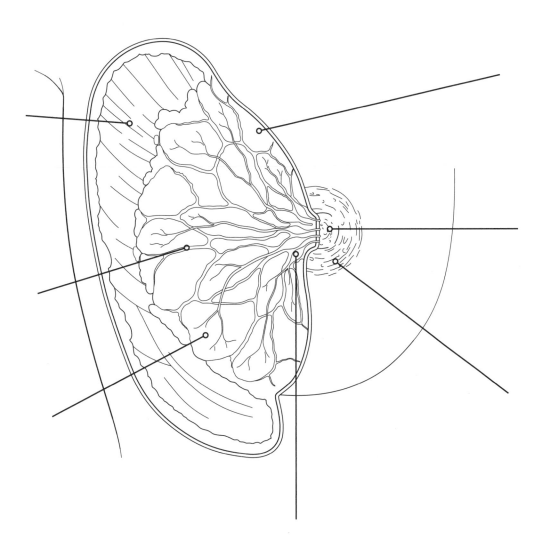

Lymphatic drainage of the breast

Lymph, the fluid that leaks out of blood vessels into the spaces between cells, is returned to the blood circulation by the lymphatic system. Lymph passes through a series of lymph nodes, which act as filters to remove bacteria, cells, and other particles.

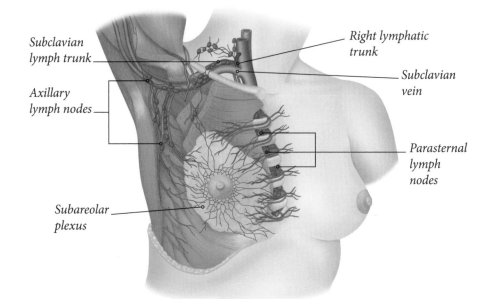

Subclavian lymph trunk

Axillary lymph nodes

Subareolar plexus

Right lymphatic trunk

Subclavian vein

Parasternal lymph nodes

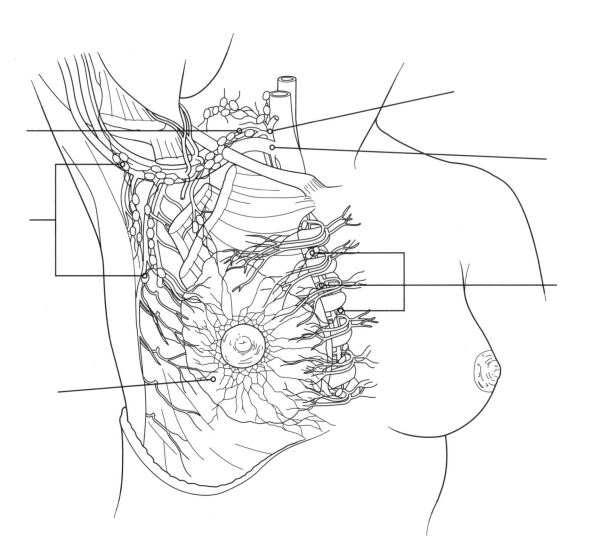

Diaphragm

The diaphragm is a sheet of muscle that separates the thorax from the abdominal cavity. It is essential for breathing as its contraction expands the chest cavity, allowing air to enter.

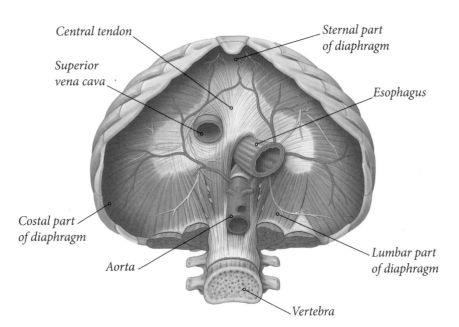

Central tendon

Sternal part of diaphragm

Superior vena cava

Esophagus

Costal part of diaphragm

Lumbar part of diaphragm

Aorta

Vertebra

Thoracic surface of the diaphragm

The upper aspect of the diaphragm is convex and forms the floor of the thoracic (chest) cavity. It is perforated by major vessels and structures that must pass through the muscle sheet in order to reach the abdomen.

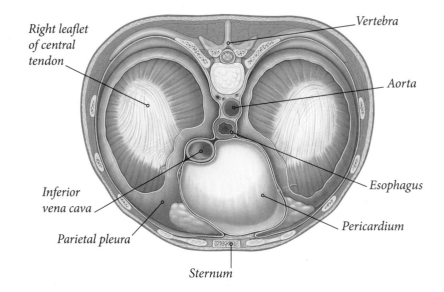

Right leaflet of central tendon

Vertebra

Aorta

Esophagus

Pericardium

Inferior vena cava

Parietal pleura

Sternum

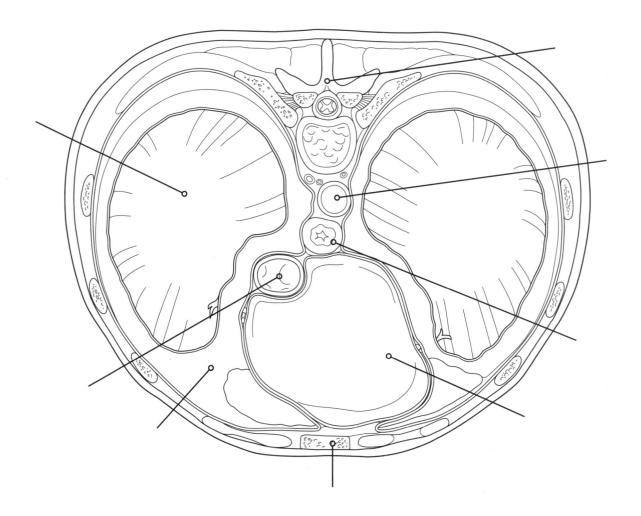

Lungs

The paired lungs are cone-shaped organs of respiration that occupy the thoracic cavity, lying to either side of the heart, great blood vessels and other structures of the central mediastinum.

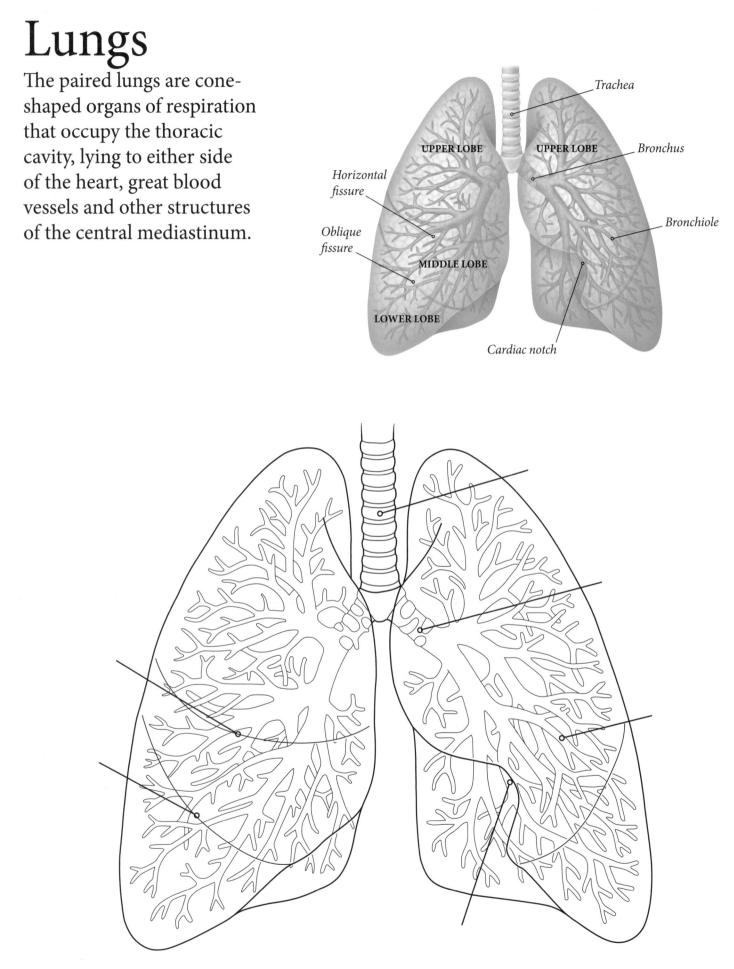

Trachea

UPPER LOBE

UPPER LOBE

Bronchus

Horizontal fissure

Bronchiole

Oblique fissure

MIDDLE LOBE

LOWER LOBE

Cardiac notch

The pleura

The lungs are covered by a thin membrane known as the pleura. The pleura lines both the outer surface of the lung and the inner surface of the thoracic cage.

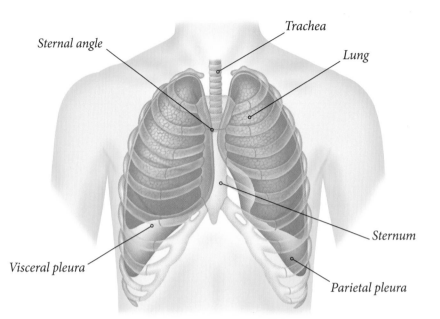

Sternal angle

Trachea

Lung

Sternum

Visceral pleura

Parietal pleura

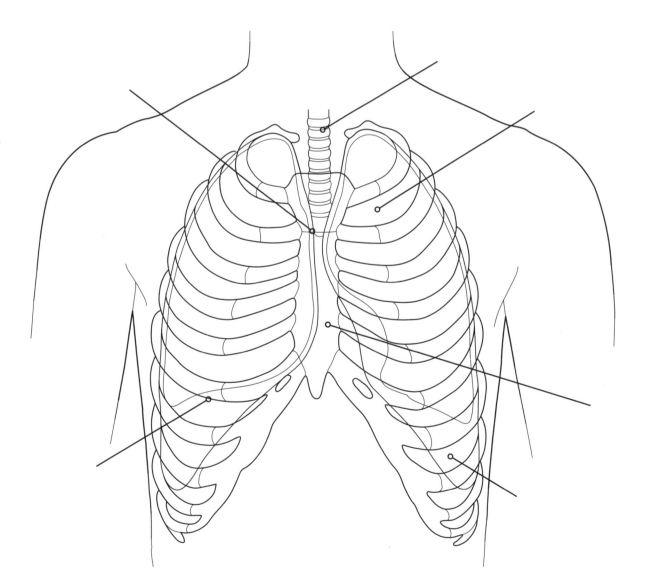

Respiratory airways

The airways form a network along which air travels to, from and within the lungs. The airways branch repeatedly, each branch narrowing until the end terminals—the alveoli—are reached.

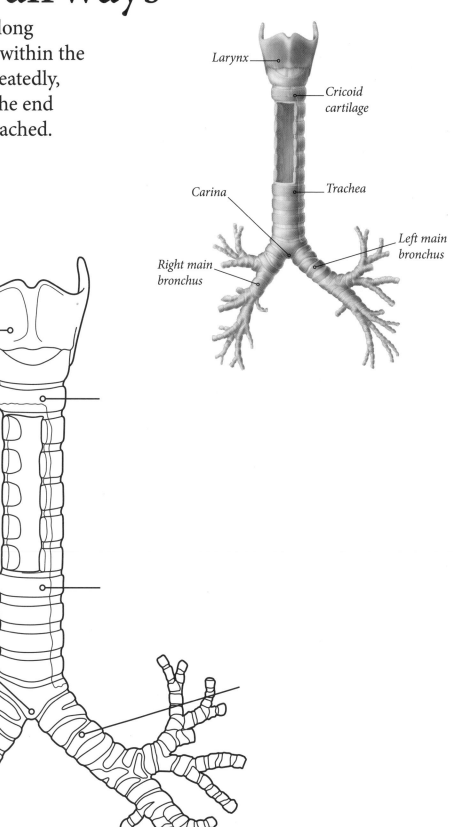

Larynx

Cricoid cartilage

Carina

Trachea

Right main bronchus

Left main bronchus

Smaller airways and alveoli

On entering the lung the main bronchus divides again and again, forming the "bronchial tree," which takes air to all parts of the lung.

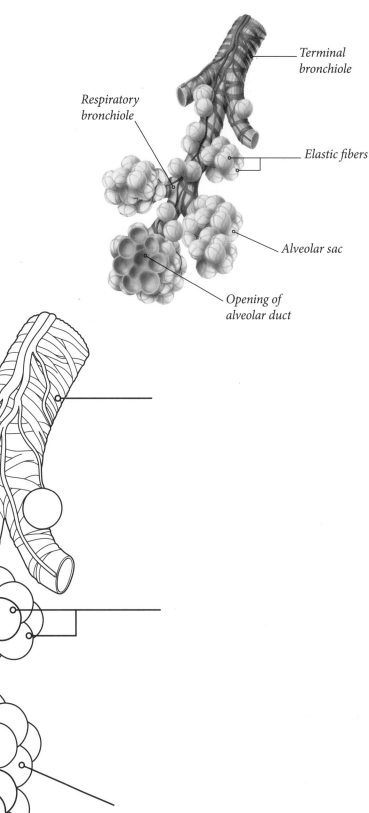

Terminal
bronchiole

Respiratory
bronchiole

Elastic fibers

Alveolar sac

Opening of
alveolar duct

Vessels of the lungs

The primary function of the lungs is to reoxygenate the blood used by the tissues of the body and to remove accumulated waste carbon dioxide. This is effected via the pulmonary blood circulation.

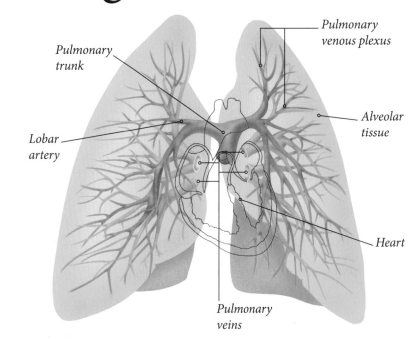

Pulmonary venous plexus

Pulmonary trunk

Alveolar tissue

Lobar artery

Heart

Pulmonary veins

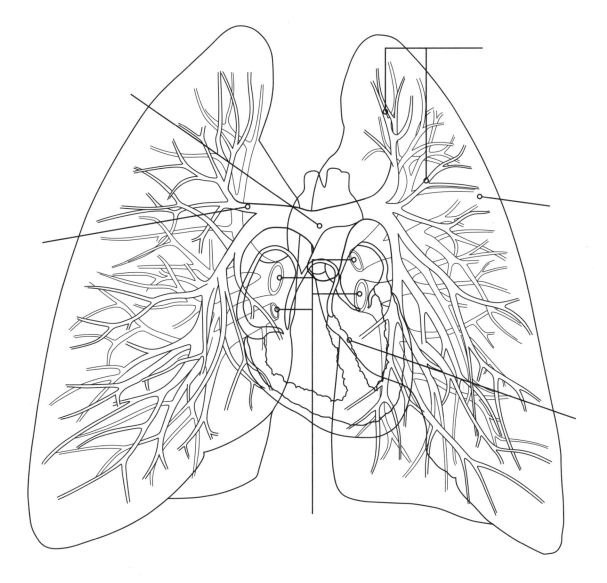

Lymphatics of the lung

Lymphatic drainage of the lung originates in two main networks, or plexuses: the superficial (subpleural) plexus and the deep lymphatic plexus. These communicate freely with each other.

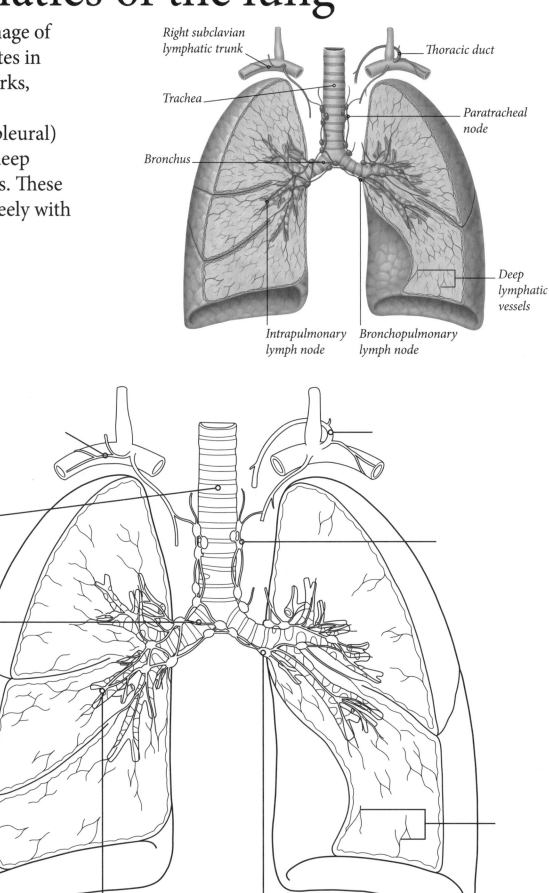

Right subclavian lymphatic trunk

Thoracic duct

Trachea

Paratracheal node

Bronchus

Deep lymphatic vessels

Intrapulmonary lymph node

Bronchopulmonary lymph node

Heart

The adult heart is about the size of a clenched fist and lies within the mediastinum in the thoracic cavity. It rests on the central tendon of the diaphragm and is flanked on either side by the lungs.

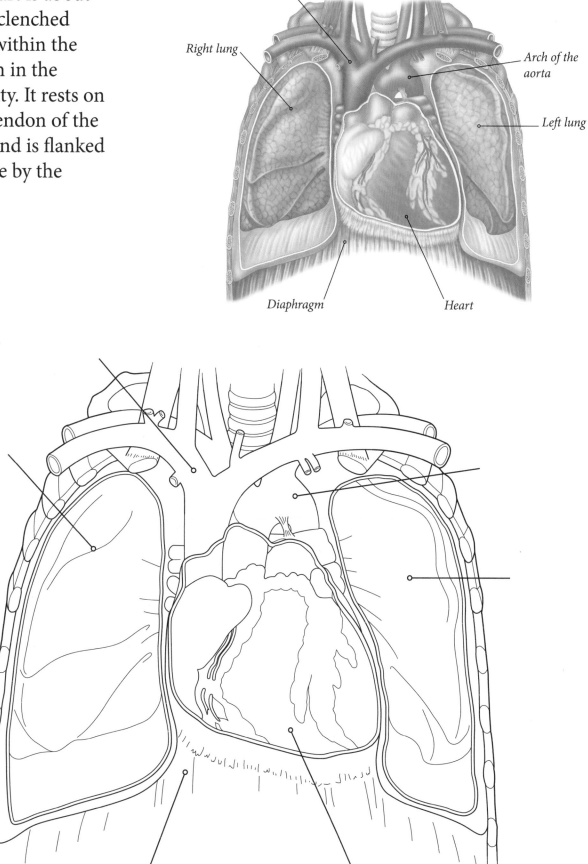

Superior vena cava

Right lung

Arch of the aorta

Left lung

Diaphragm

Heart

The pericardium

The heart is enclosed within a protective triple-walled bag of connective tissue called the pericardium. The pericardium is composed of two parts, the fibrous pericardium and the serous pericardium.

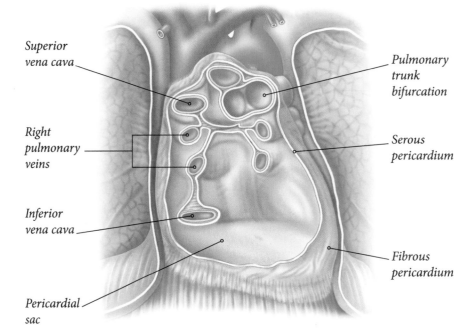

Superior vena cava

Pulmonary trunk bifurcation

Right pulmonary veins

Serous pericardium

Inferior vena cava

Fibrous pericardium

Pericardial sac

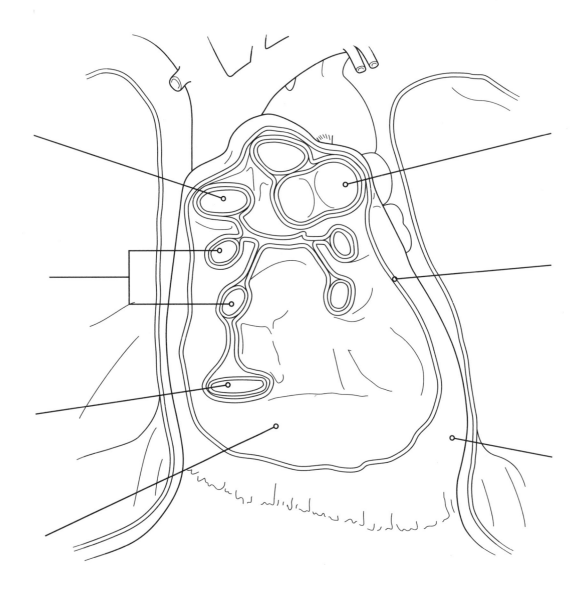

Chambers of the heart

The heart is divided into four chambers: two thin-walled atria, which receive venous blood, and two larger, thick-walled ventricles, which pump blood into the arterial system.

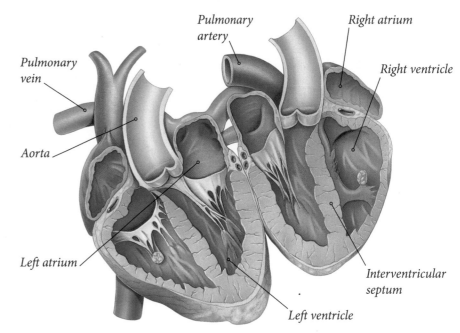

Pulmonary artery

Right atrium

Pulmonary vein

Right ventricle

Aorta

Left atrium

Interventricular septum

Left ventricle

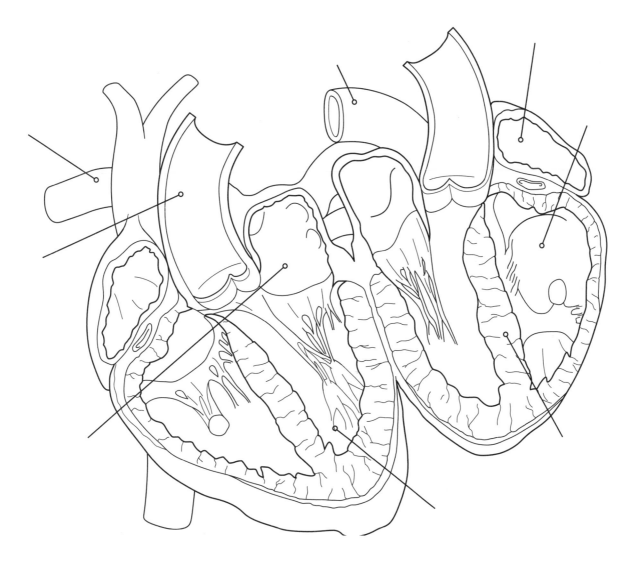

The atria

The atria are the two smaller, thin-walled chambers of the heart. They sit above the ventricles separated by the atrioventricular valves.

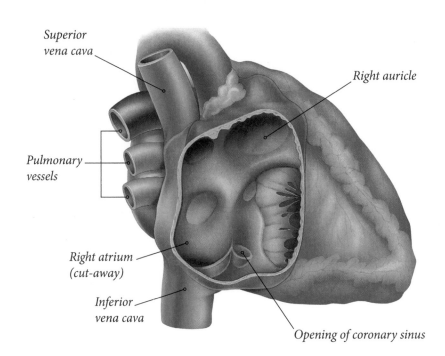

Superior vena cava

Right auricle

Pulmonary vessels

Right atrium (cut-away)

Inferior vena cava

Opening of coronary sinus

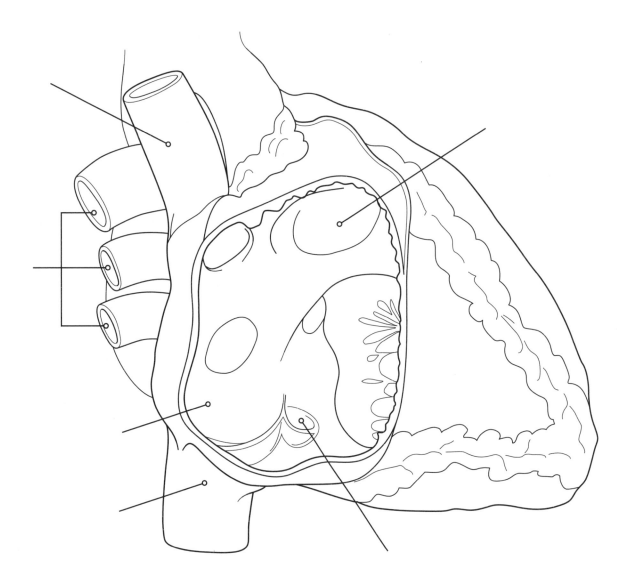

Valves of the heart

The heart is a powerful muscular pump through which blood flows in a forward direction only. Backflow is prevented by the four heart valves, which have a vital role in maintaining the circulation.

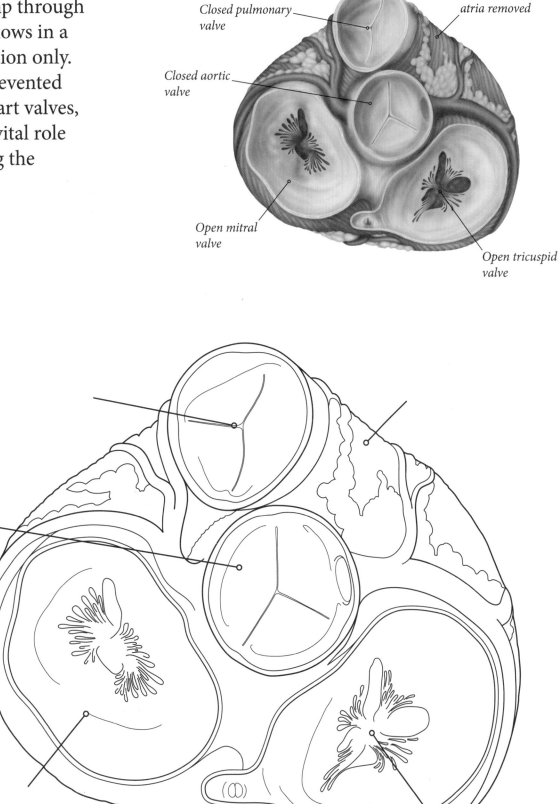

Closed pulmonary valve

Heart at rest with atria removed

Closed aortic valve

Open mitral valve

Open tricuspid valve

Aortic and pulmonary valves

The pulmonary and aortic valves are also known as the semilunar valves. They guard the route of exit of blood from the heart, preventing backflow of blood into the ventricles as they relax after a contraction.

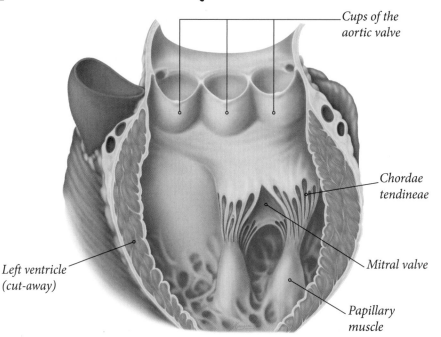

Cups of the aortic valve

Chordae tendineae

Mitral valve

Left ventricle (cut-away)

Papillary muscle

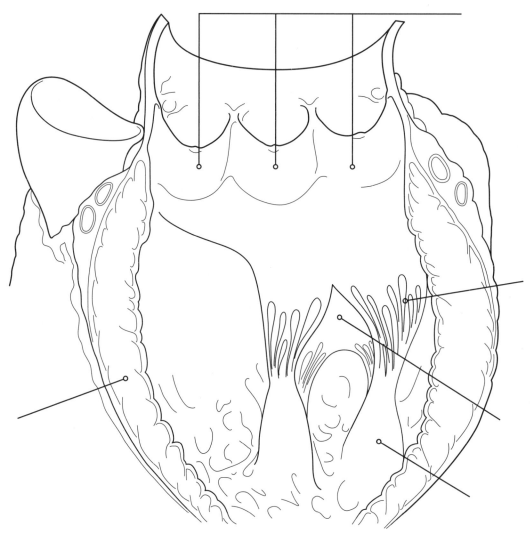

Vessels of the heart

Blood is delivered to the
heart by two large veins—
the superior and inferior
venae cavae—and pumped
out into the aorta. The
venae cavae and aorta are
collectively known as the
great vessels.

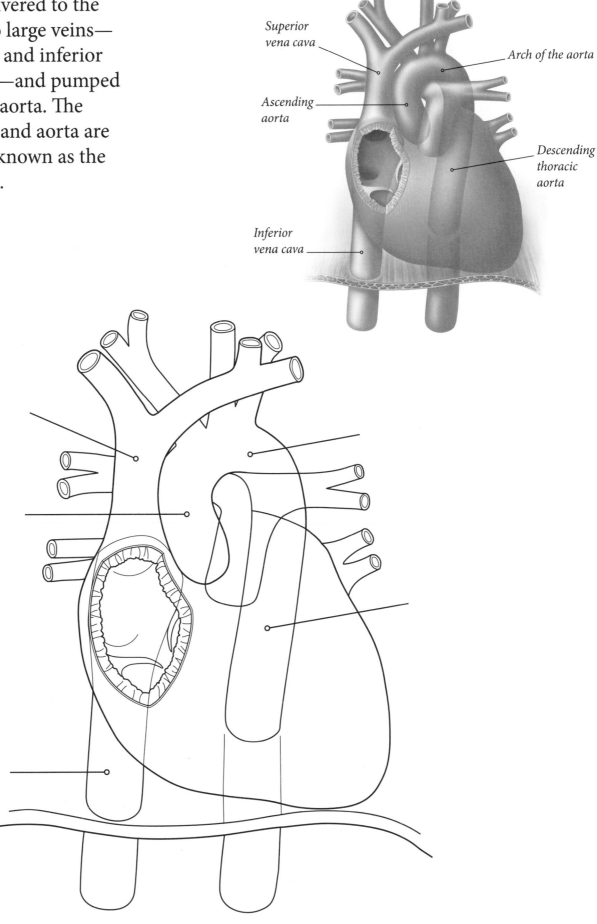

Superior vena cava

Arch of the aorta

Ascending aorta

Descending thoracic aorta

Inferior vena cava

Supplying blood to the heart

The heart muscle itself and the coverings of the heart need their own blood supply, which is provided by the coronary arteries.

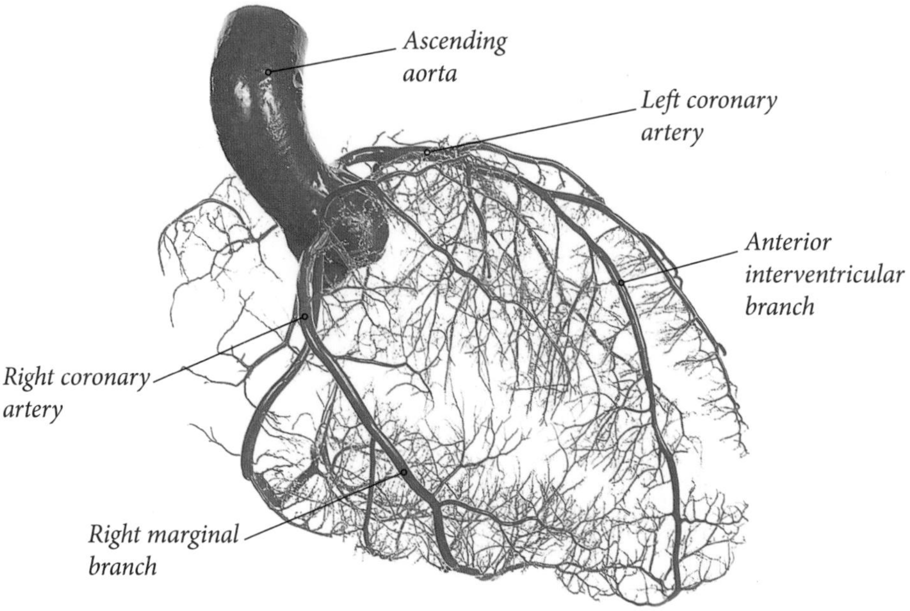

Ascending
aorta

Left coronary
artery

Anterior
interventricular
branch

Right coronary
artery

Right marginal
branch

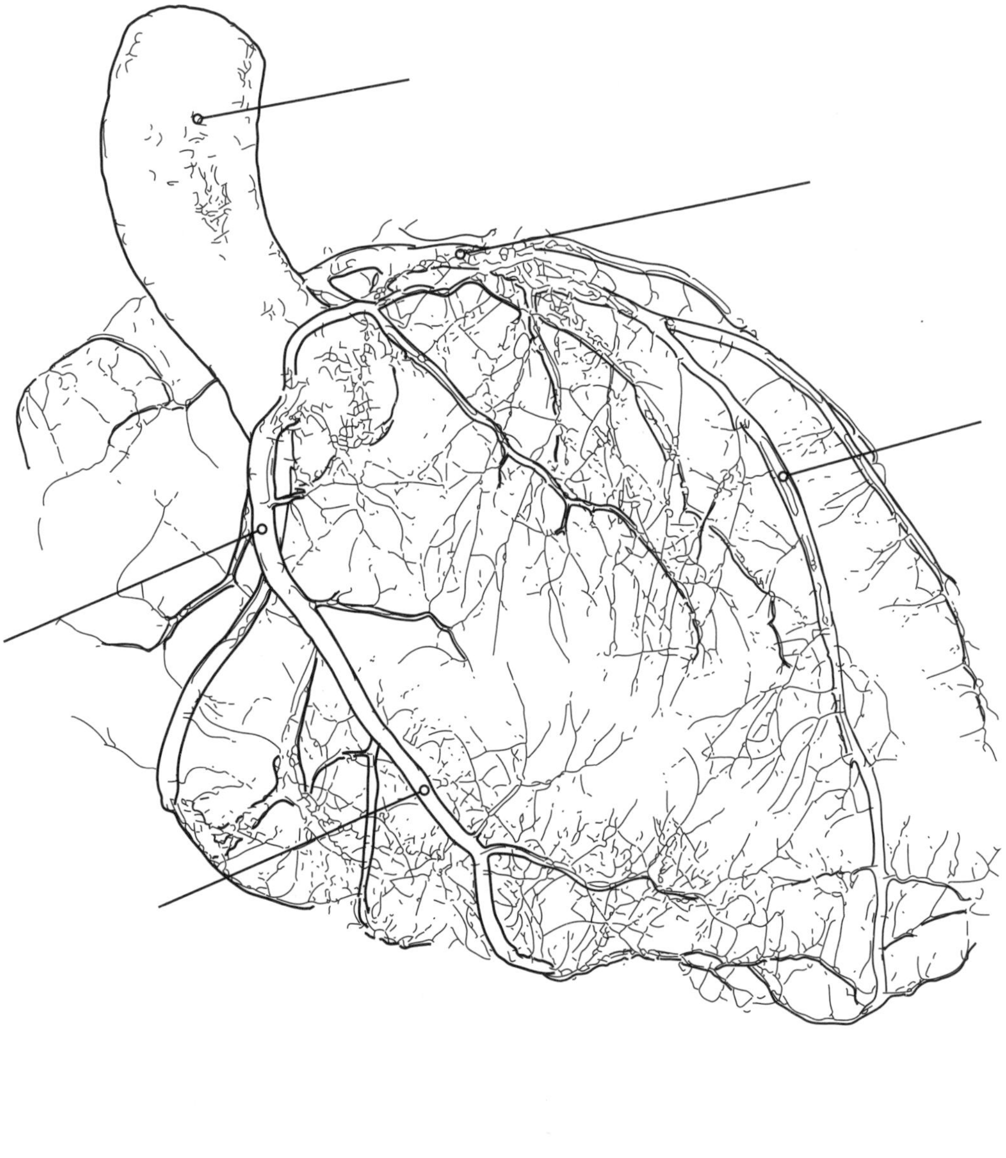

Conducting system of the heart

When the body is at rest, the heart beats at a rate of about 70 to 80 beats per minute. Within its muscular walls, a conducting system sets the pace and ensures that the muscle contracts in a coordinated way.

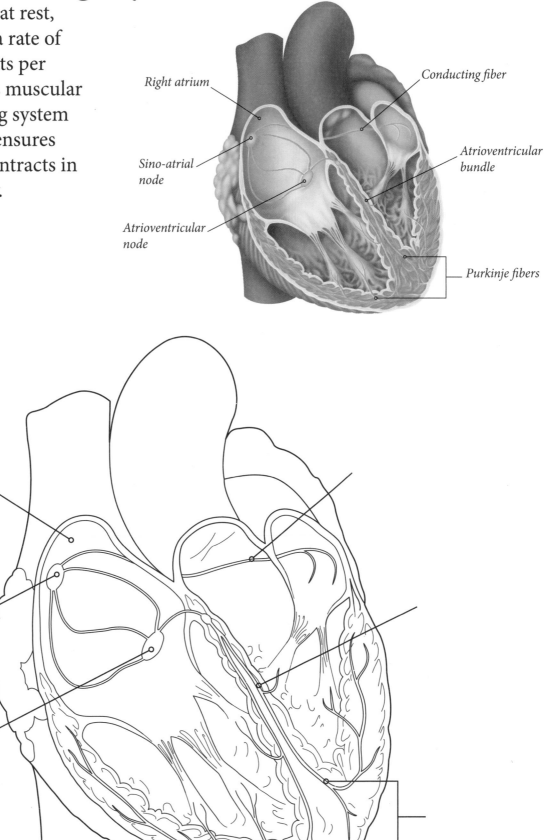

Right atrium

Conducting fiber

Sino-atrial node

Atrioventricular bundle

Atrioventricular node

Purkinje fibers

Cardiac cycle

The cardiac cycle is the series of changes within the heart that causes blood to be pumped around the body. It is divided into a period when heart muscle contracts, known as systole and a period when it is relaxed, known as diastole.

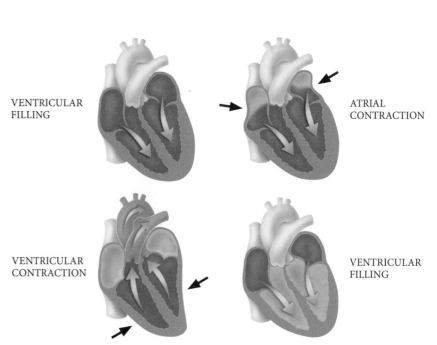

VENTRICULAR FILLING

ATRIAL CONTRACTION

VENTRICULAR CONTRACTION

VENTRICULAR FILLING

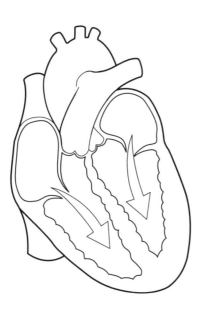

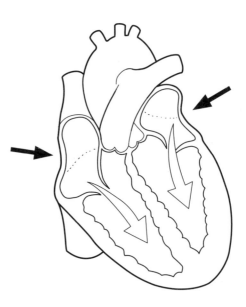

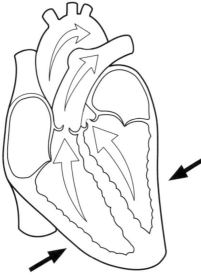

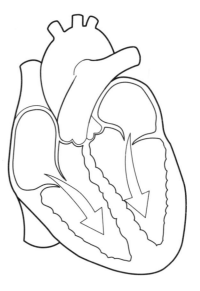

Shoulder joint

The glenohumeral, or shoulder joint, is a ball-and-socket joint at the point of articulation of the humerus and the scapula. The construction of this joint allows the arm a wide range of movement.

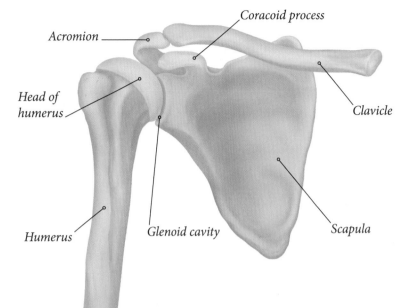

Coracoid process

Acromion

Head of humerus

Clavicle

Humerus

Glenoid cavity

Scapula

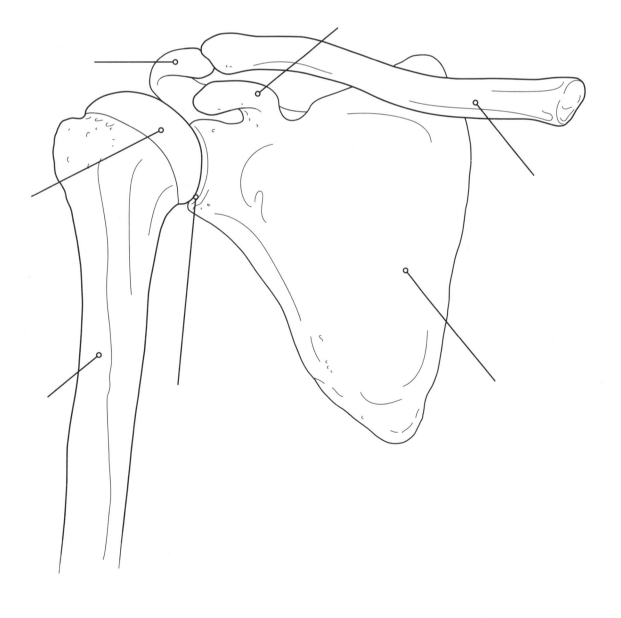

Ligaments of the shoulder joint

The ligaments of the shoulder joint, along with the surrounding muscles, are crucial for the stability of this shallow ball-and-socket joint.

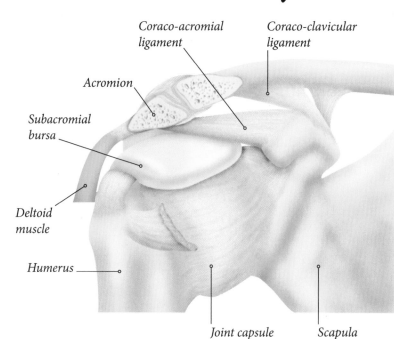

Coraco-acromial ligament

Coraco-clavicular ligament

Acromion

Subacromial bursa

Deltoid muscle

Humerus

Joint capsule

Scapula

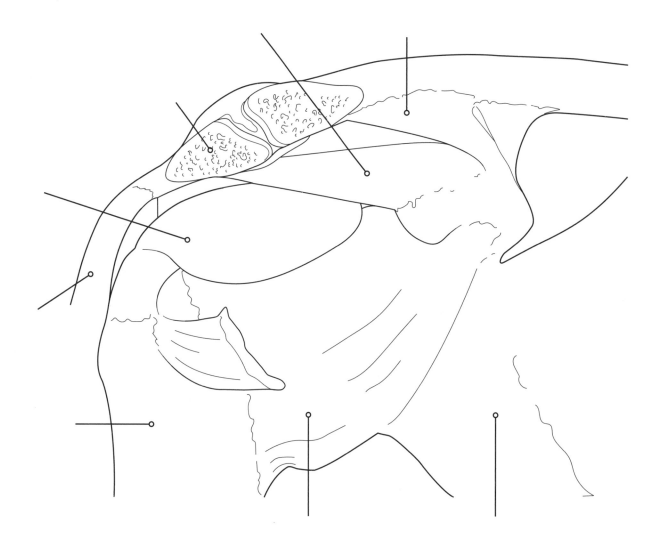

Movements of the shoulder joint

The shoulder joint is a ball-and-socket joint which allows 360° of movement to give maximum flexibility. In addition to enabling these movements, the muscles of the pectoral girdle add stability.

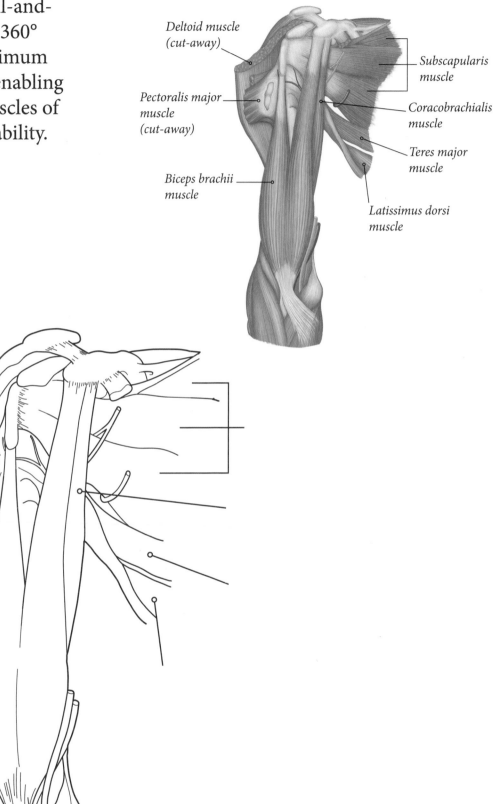

Deltoid muscle (cut-away)

Pectoralis major muscle (cut-away)

Biceps brachii muscle

Subscapularis muscle

Coracobrachialis muscle

Teres major muscle

Latissimus dorsi muscle

Rotation of the arm and "rotator cuff"

The rotator cuff muscles include subscapularis, supraspinatus, infraspinatus, and teres minor. These muscles act to strengthen and increase the stability of the shoulder joint. They also act individually to move the humerus and upper arm.

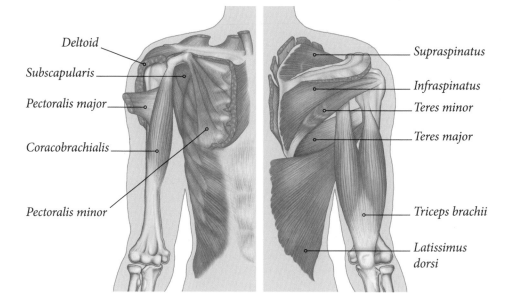

Deltoid

Subscapularis

Pectoralis major

Coracobrachialis

Pectoralis minor

Supraspinatus

Infraspinatus

Teres minor

Teres major

Triceps brachii

Latissimus dorsi

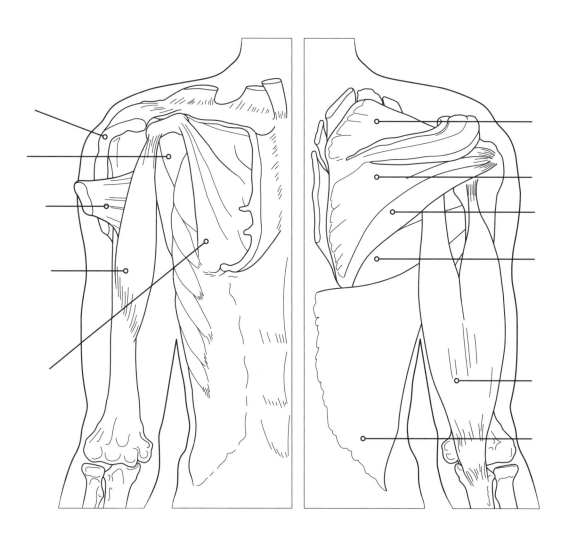

Axilla

The axilla, or armpit, is a roughly pyramidal space where the upper arm joins the thorax. It contains a number of important structures, such as blood vessels and nerves passing to and from the upper limb.

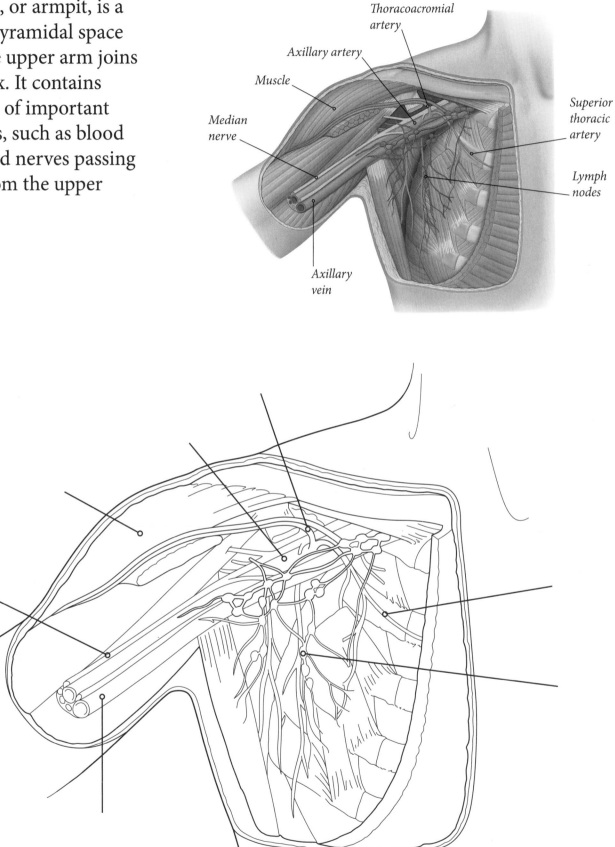

Thoracoacromial artery

Axillary artery

Muscle

Median nerve

Superior thoracic artery

Lymph nodes

Axillary vein

Structure of the humerus

The humerus, a typical "long bone," is found in the upper arm. It has a long shaft with expanded ends that connect with the scapula at the shoulder joint and the radius and ulna at the elbow.

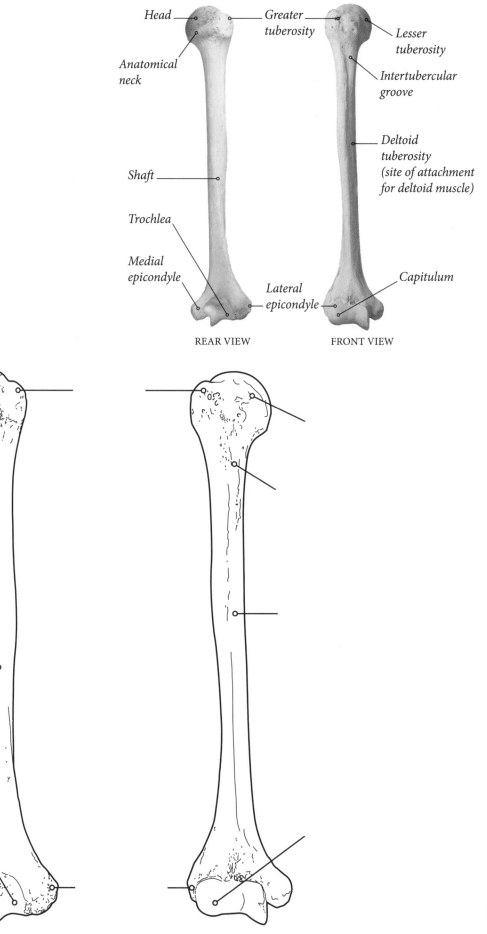

Head

Greater tuberosity

Lesser tuberosity

Anatomical neck

Intertubercular groove

Deltoid tuberosity (site of attachment for deltoid muscle)

Shaft

Trochlea

Medial epicondyle

Lateral epicondyle

Capitulum

REAR VIEW

FRONT VIEW

Inside the humerus

The structure of the humerus is typical of the long bones. The bone is divided into the diaphysis (shaft) and the epiphysis (head) at either end.

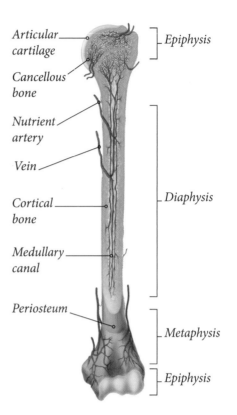

Articular cartilage

Cancellous bone

Nutrient artery

Vein

Cortical bone

Medullary canal

Periosteum

Epiphysis

Diaphysis

Metaphysis

Epiphysis

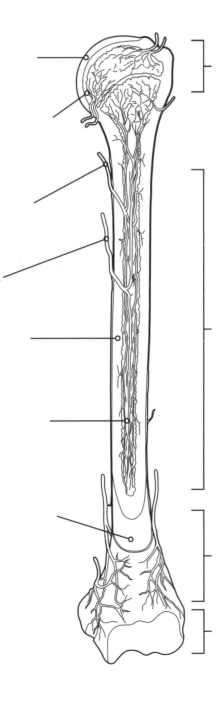

Ulna

The ulna and the radius are the long bones of the forearm. They articulate with the humerus and the wrist bones and are uniquely adapted to enable rotation of the hand and forearm.

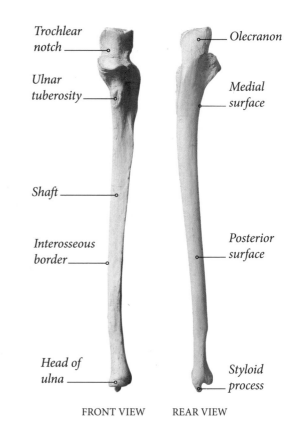

Trochlear notch

Ulnar tuberosity

Shaft

Interosseous border

Head of ulna

Olecranon

Medial surface

Posterior surface

Styloid process

FRONT VIEW   REAR VIEW

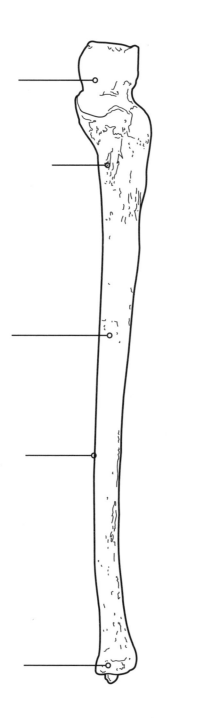

Radius

The radius is the shorter of the two bones of the forearm and articulates with the wrist. It is joined firmly to the ulna by a tough layer of connective tissue.

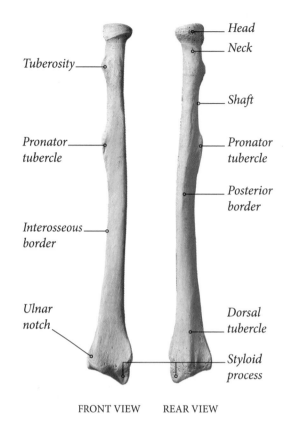

Head
Neck
Tuberosity
Shaft
Pronator tubercle
Pronator tubercle
Posterior border
Interosseous border
Ulnar notch
Dorsal tubercle
Styloid process

FRONT VIEW   REAR VIEW

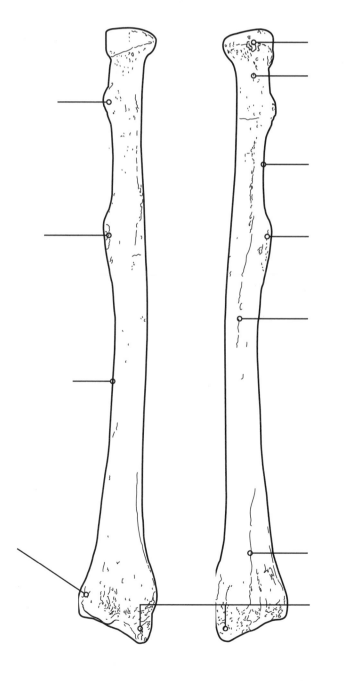

Elbow

The elbow is the fluid-filled joint where the humerus of the upper arm and the radius and ulna of the forearm articulate. The joint structure only allows hinge-like movement but is extremely stable.

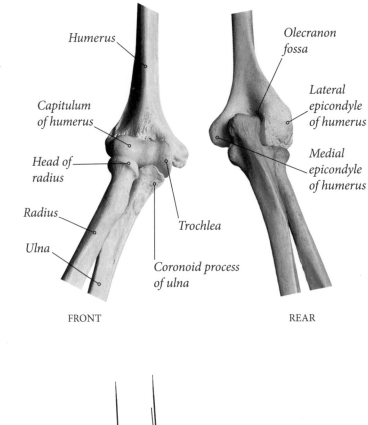

Humerus

Capitulum of humerus

Head of radius

Radius

Ulna

Trochlea

Coronoid process of ulna

Olecranon fossa

Lateral epicondyle of humerus

Medial epicondyle of humerus

FRONT

REAR

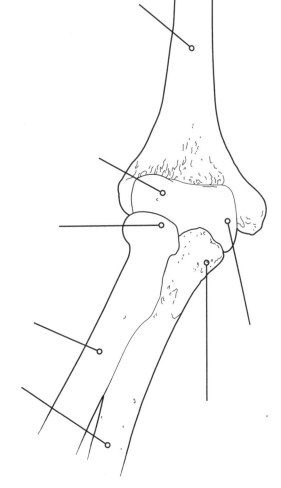

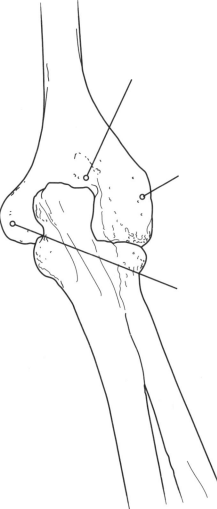

Ligaments of the elbow

The elbow is supported
and strengthened at each
side by the strong collateral
ligaments. These are
thickenings of the joint
capsule.

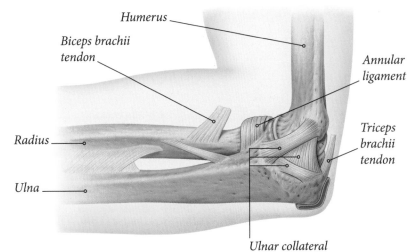

Humerus

Biceps brachii
tendon

Annular
ligament

Radius

Triceps
brachii
tendon

Ulna

Ulnar collateral
ligament

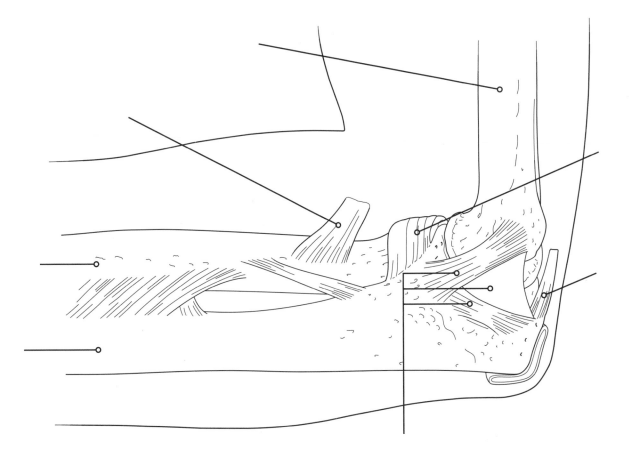

Muscles of the upper arm

The musculature of the upper arm is divided into two distinct compartments. The muscles of the anterior compartment act to flex the arm and the muscles of the posterior compartment extend it.

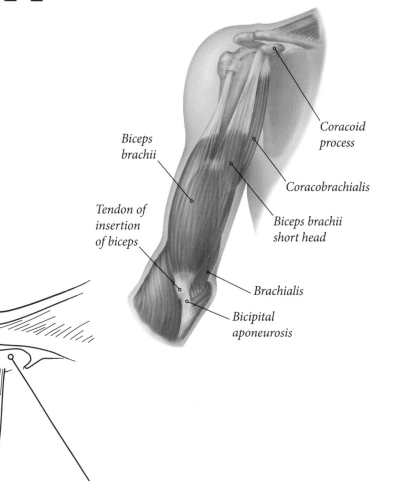

Biceps brachii

Coracoid process

Coracobrachialis

Tendon of insertion of biceps

Biceps brachii short head

Brachialis

Bicipital aponeurosis

Muscles of the posterior compartment

The muscles of the back of the upper arm act to extend the elbow, so straightening the forearm with the upper arm.

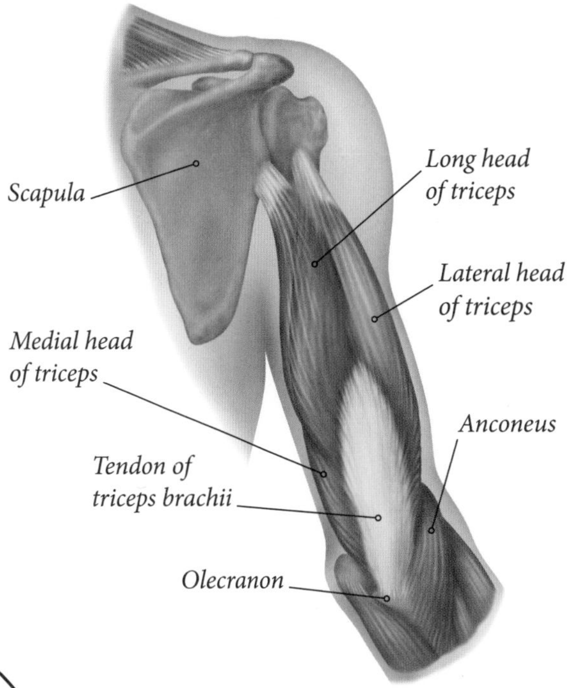

Scapula

Long head of triceps

Lateral head of triceps

Medial head of triceps

Anconeus

Tendon of triceps brachii

Olecranon

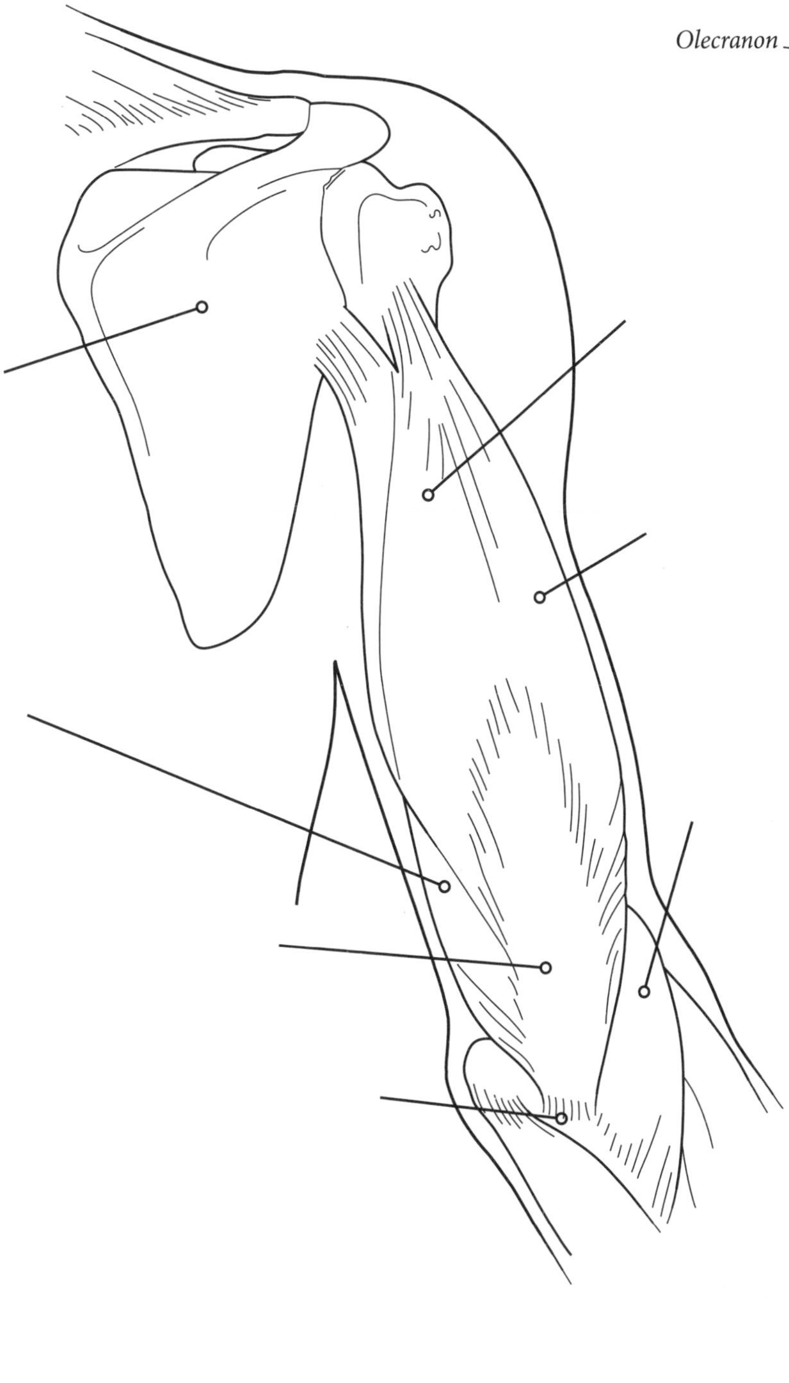

Muscles of the forearm

The flexor muscles of the front compartment of the forearm act to flex the hand, wrist, and fingers. They are divided into superficial and deep muscles of the flexor and extensor compartments.

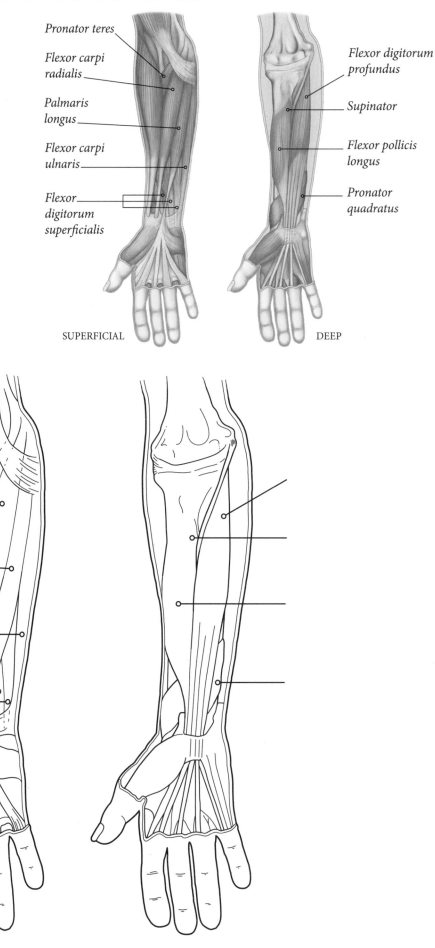

Pronator teres

Flexor carpi radialis

Palmaris longus

Flexor carpi ulnaris

Flexor digitorum superficialis

Flexor digitorum profundus

Supinator

Flexor pollicis longus

Pronator quadratus

SUPERFICIAL

DEEP

Flexing the hand

The muscles of the forearm
are divided into front and
rear compartments. The
front flexor muscles bend
the wrist and fingers and the
rear extensor muscles act to
straighten them again.

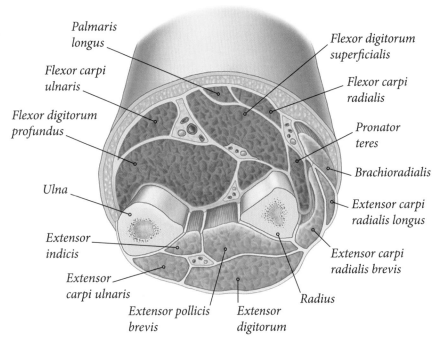

Palmaris
longus

Flexor carpi
ulnaris

Flexor digitorum
profundus

Ulna

Extensor
indicis

Extensor
carpi ulnaris

Extensor pollicis
brevis

Extensor
digitorum

Radius

Flexor digitorum
superficialis

Flexor carpi
radialis

Pronator
teres

Brachioradialis

Extensor carpi
radialis longus

Extensor carpi
radialis brevis

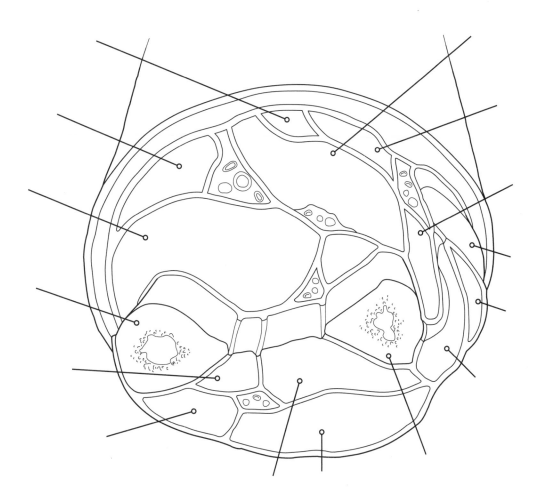

Blood vessels of the arm

The arteries of the arm supply blood
to the soft tissues and bones. The
main arteries divide to form many
smaller vessels that communicate
at networks—anastomoses—at the
elbow and wrist.

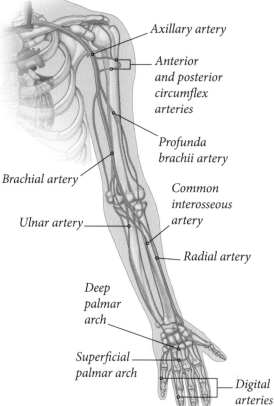

Axillary artery

*Anterior
and posterior
circumflex
arteries*

*Profunda
brachii artery*

Brachial artery

*Common
interosseous
artery*

Ulnar artery

Radial artery

*Deep
palmar
arch*

*Superficial
palmar arch*

*Digital
arteries*

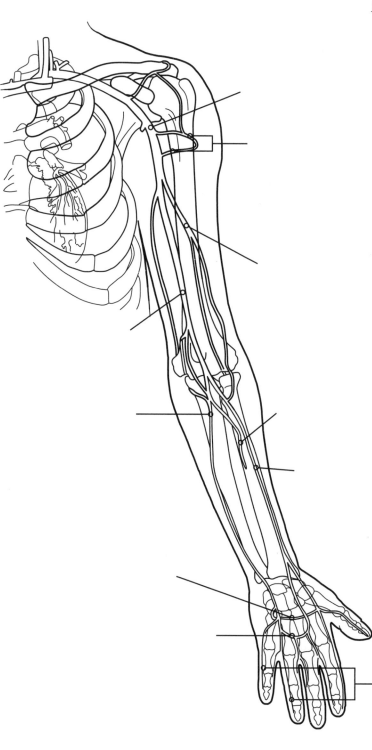

Veins of the arm

The veins of the arm are divided
into deep and superficial veins.
The superficial veins lie close to
the skin's surface and are often
easily visible.

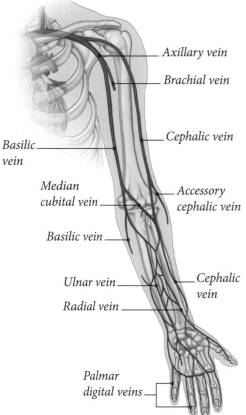

Axillary vein

Brachial vein

Cephalic vein

Basilic vein

Median cubital vein

Accessory cephalic vein

Basilic vein

Ulnar vein

Cephalic vein

Radial vein

Palmar digital veins

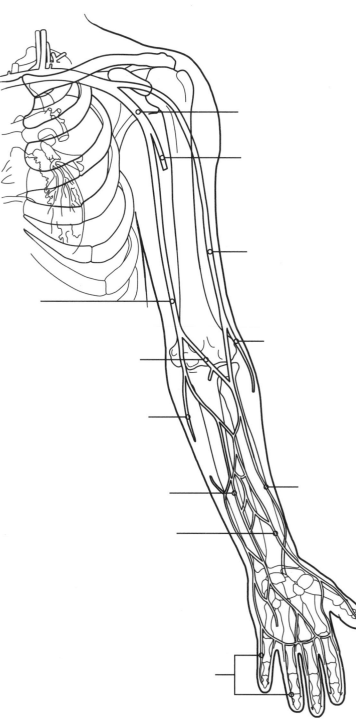

Nerves of the arm

The nerves of the arm supply the skin and muscles of the forearm and hand. There are four main nerves in the arm: the radial, musculocutaneous, median, and ulnar nerves.

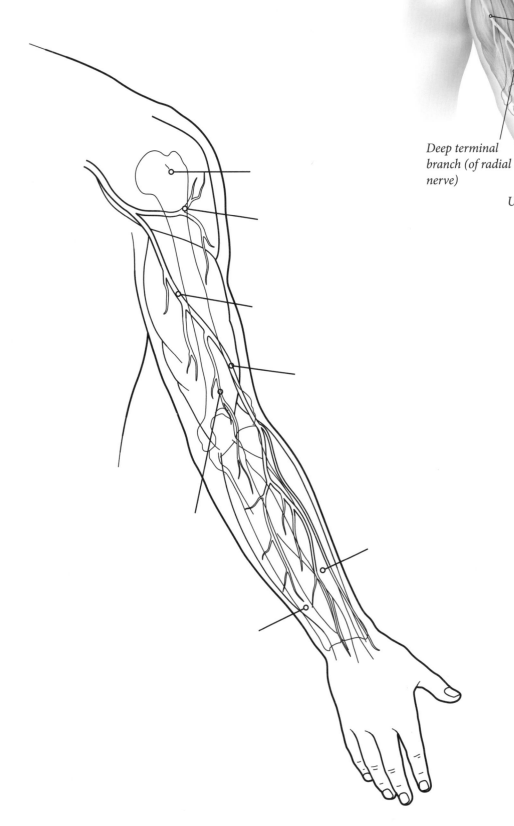

Humerus

Axillary nerve

Radial nerve

Superficial terminal branch (of radial nerve)

Deep terminal branch (of radial nerve)

Radius

Ulna

Median and ulnar nerves

The median nerve supplies the forearm muscles enabling the actions of flexion and pronation. The ulnar nerve passes behind the elbow—where it may be felt if the "funny bone" is knocked—to supply some of the small muscles of the hand.

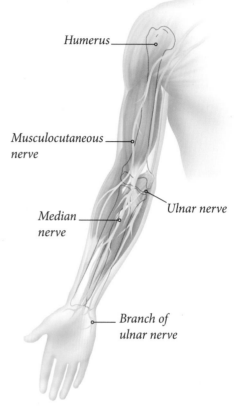

Humerus

Musculocutaneous nerve

Ulnar nerve

Median nerve

Branch of ulnar nerve

Bones of the wrist

The wrist lies between the radius and ulna of the forearm and the bones of the fingers. It is made up of eight marble-sized bones that move together to allow flexibility of the wrist joint and the hand.

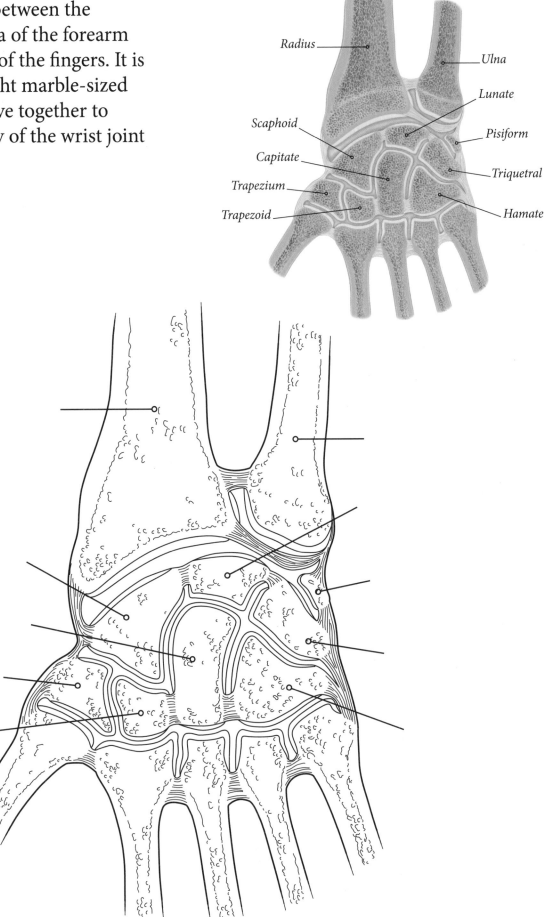

Radius

Ulna

Lunate

Scaphoid

Pisiform

Capitate

Triquetral

Trapezium

Trapezoid

Hamate

Carpal tunnel

The strong ligaments of the wrist bind together the carpal bones, allowing stability and flexibility. Within the wrist is a fibrous band through which important tendons and nerves run—the carpal tunnel.

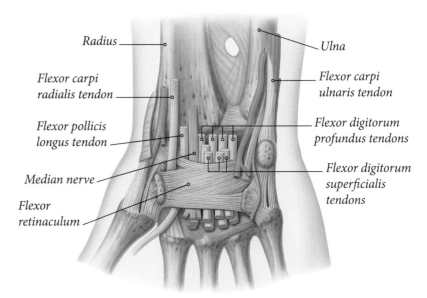

Radius

Ulna

Flexor carpi radialis tendon

Flexor carpi ulnaris tendon

Flexor pollicis longus tendon

Flexor digitorum profundus tendons

Median nerve

Flexor digitorum superficialis tendons

Flexor retinaculum

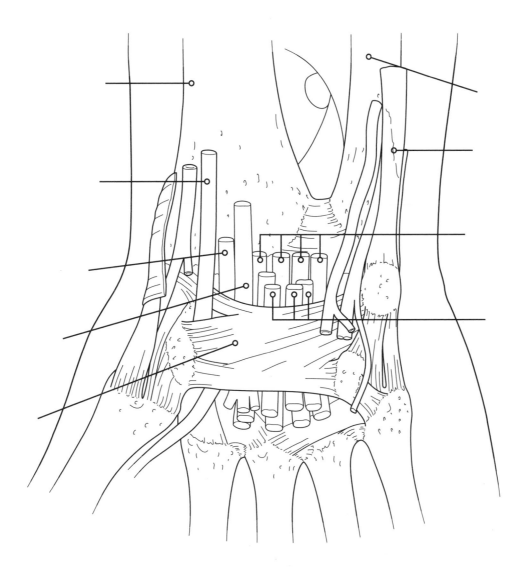

Ligaments of the wrist

The ligaments of the wrist joint are thickenings of the joint capsule that help tie the wrist strongly to the lower ends of the radius and ulna.

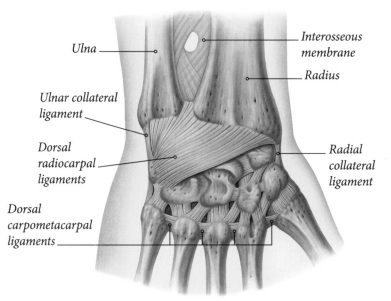

Ulna

Interosseous membrane

Radius

Ulnar collateral ligament

Dorsal radiocarpal ligaments

Radial collateral ligament

Dorsal carpometacarpal ligaments

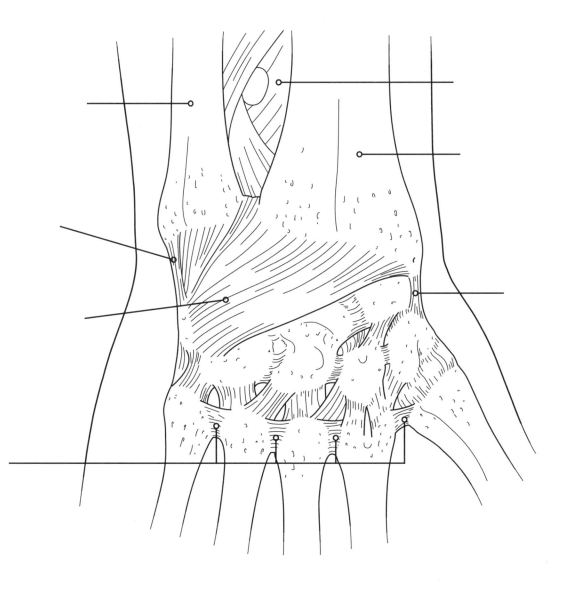

Bones of the hand

The bones of the hand are divided into the metacarpal bones that support the palm and the phalanges or finger bones. The joints of these bones allow the fingers and the thumb great mobility.

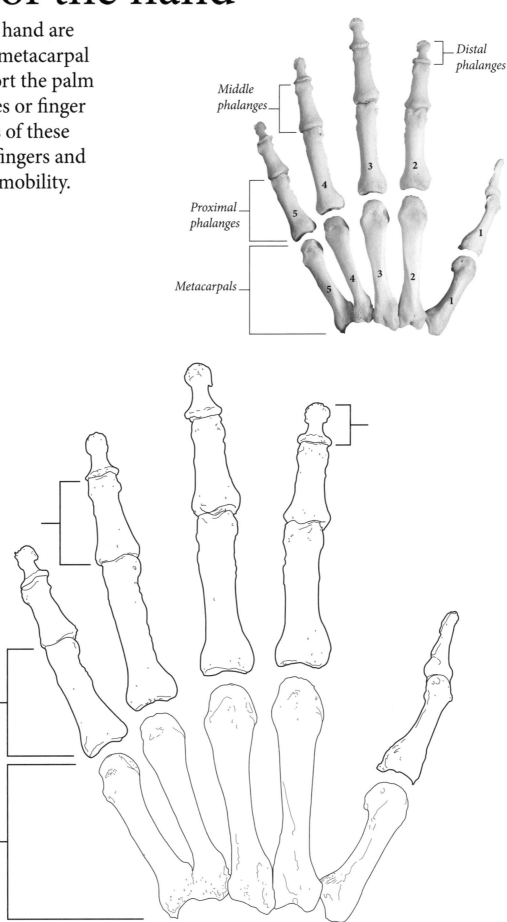

Distal phalanges

Middle phalanges

Proximal phalanges

Metacarpals

Finger joints

The joints between the
phalanges are surrounded
by fibrous capsules, lined
with synovial membrane
and supported by strong
collateral ligaments.

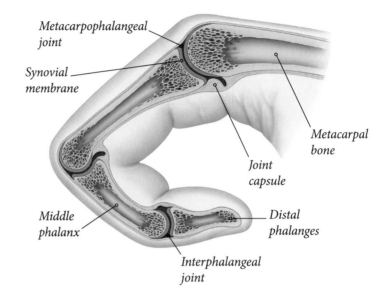

Metacarpophalangeal joint

Synovial membrane

Metacarpal bone

Joint capsule

Middle phalanx

Distal phalanges

Interphalangeal joint

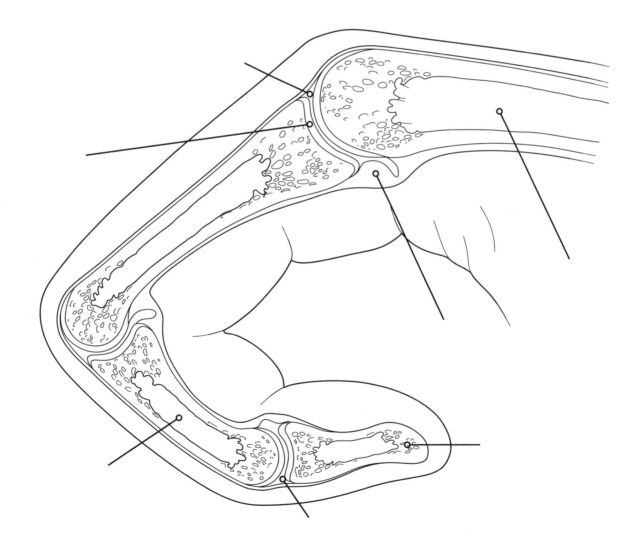

Muscles of the hand

The human hand is an exceptionally versatile structure, capable of powerful and delicate movements. These are produced by the actions and interactions of the numerous muscles that act upon it.

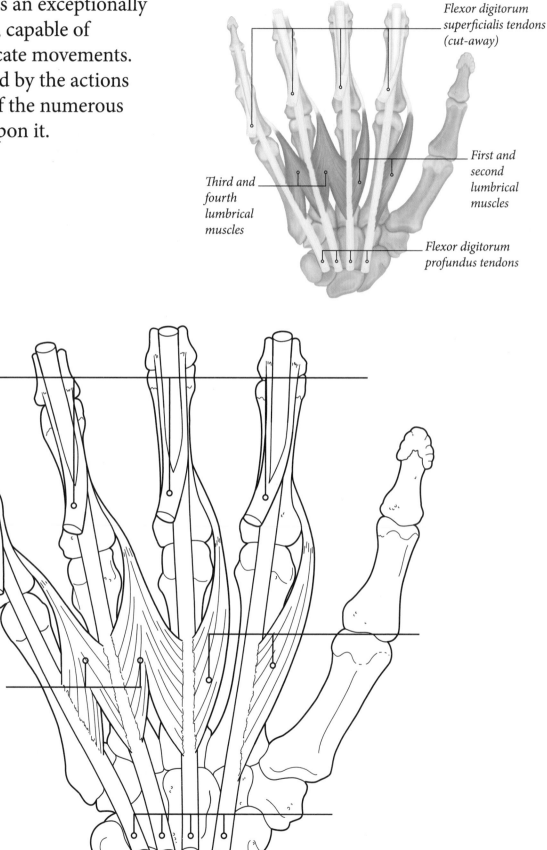

Flexor digitorum superficialis tendons (cut-away)

First and second lumbrical muscles

Third and fourth lumbrical muscles

Flexor digitorum profundus tendons

Moving the thumb and little finger

The muscles that move the thumb are contained in the thenar eminence, at the base of the thumb; those that move the little finger are found in the hypothenar eminence, between the little finger and the wrist.

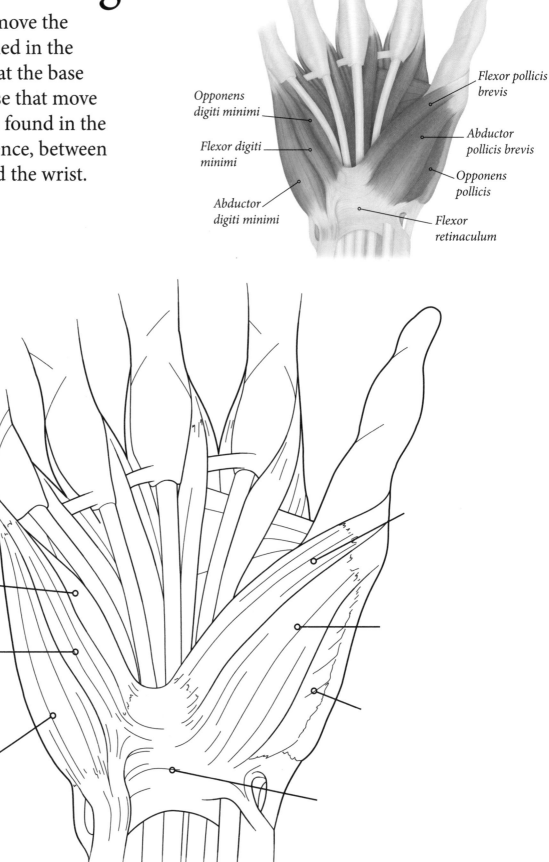

Opponens digiti minimi

Flexor digiti minimi

Abductor digiti minimi

Flexor pollicis brevis

Abductor pollicis brevis

Opponens pollicis

Flexor retinaculum

Blood vessels of the hand

The hand is supplied with numerous arteries and veins. These join to form networks of small, interconnecting blood vessels that ensure a good blood supply to all fingers, even if one artery is damaged.

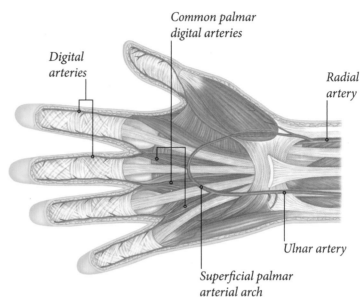

Digital arteries

Common palmar digital arteries

Radial artery

Ulnar artery

Superficial palmar arterial arch

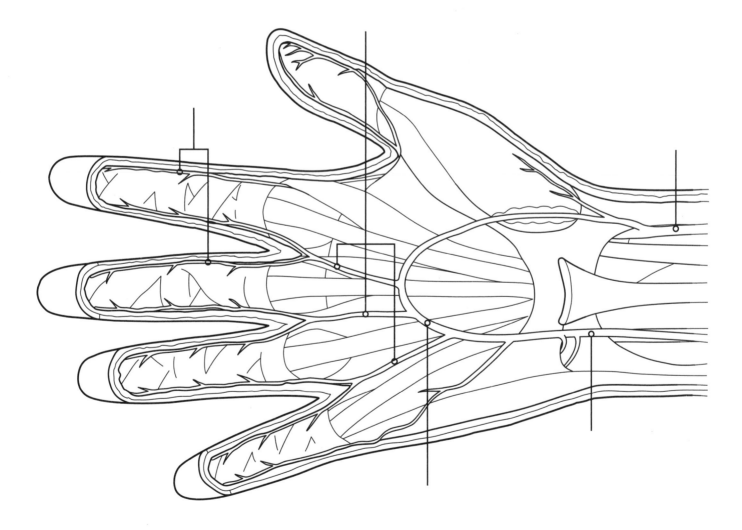

Nerves of the hand

The structures of the hand
receive their nerve supply from
terminal branches of the three
main nerves of the upper limb:
the median, ulnar, and radial
nerves.

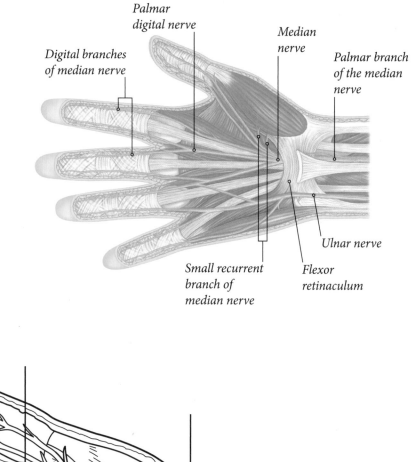

*Palmar
digital nerve*

*Median
nerve*

*Digital branches
of median nerve*

*Palmar branch
of the median
nerve*

Ulnar nerve

*Small recurrent
branch of
median nerve*

*Flexor
retinaculum*

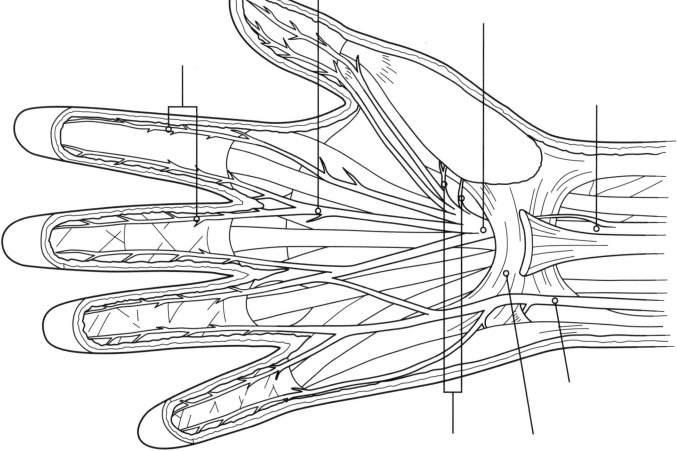

Overview of the abdomen

The abdomen is the part of the trunk which lies between the thorax (above) and the pelvis (below). The contents of the abdominal cavity are supported by a bony framework and the abdominal wall.

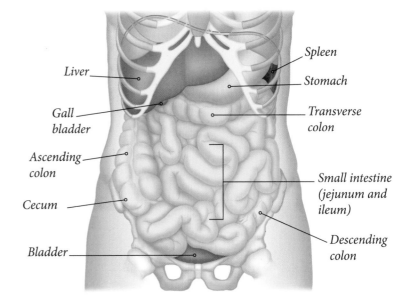

Liver

Gall bladder

Ascending colon

Cecum

Bladder

Spleen

Stomach

Transverse colon

Small intestine (jejunum and ileum)

Descending colon

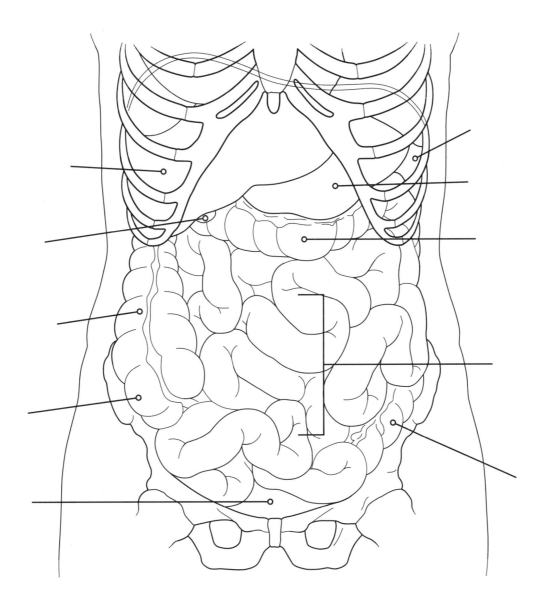

Abdominal wall

The abdominal cavity lies between the diaphragm and the pelvis. The abdominal wall at the front and sides of the body consists of different muscular layers, surrounding and supporting the cavity.

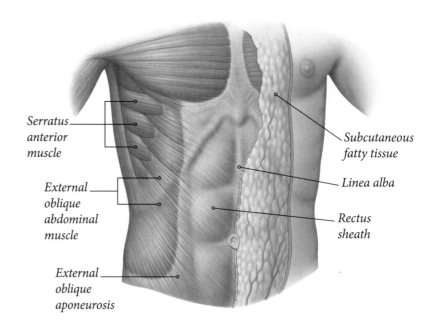

Serratus anterior muscle

External oblique abdominal muscle

External oblique aponeurosis

Subcutaneous fatty tissue

Linea alba

Rectus sheath

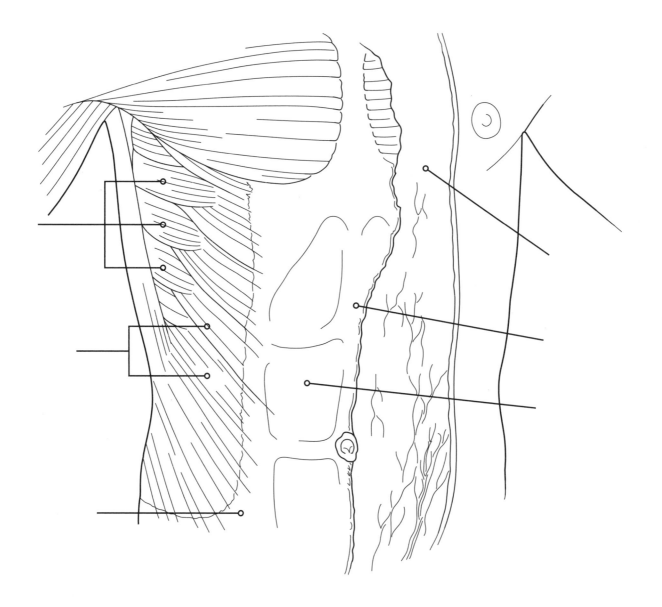

Deeper muscles of the abdominal wall

Beneath the large external oblique muscle lie two more layers of sheet-like muscle, the internal oblique and the transversus abdominis. In addition, running vertically down the center of the abdominal wall is the rectus abdominis.

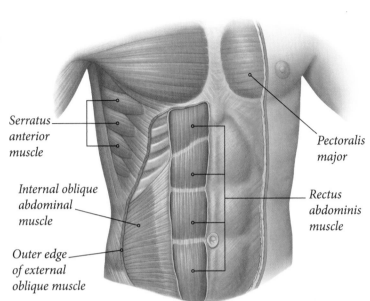

Serratus anterior muscle

Internal oblique abdominal muscle

Outer edge of external oblique muscle

Pectoralis major

Rectus abdominis muscle

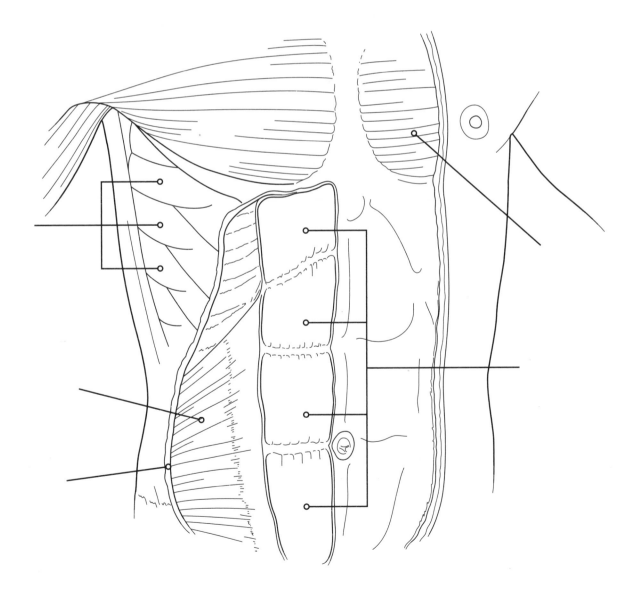

Esophagus

The esophagus is the tubular connection between the pharynx in the neck and the stomach. It is used solely as a passage for food, and plays no part in digestion and absorption.

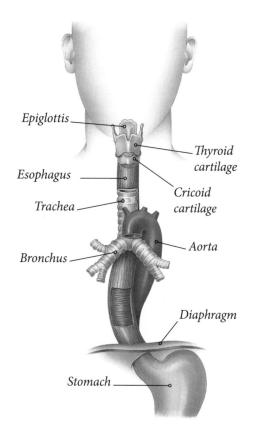

Epiglottis

Thyroid cartilage

Esophagus

Cricoid cartilage

Trachea

Aorta

Bronchus

Diaphragm

Stomach

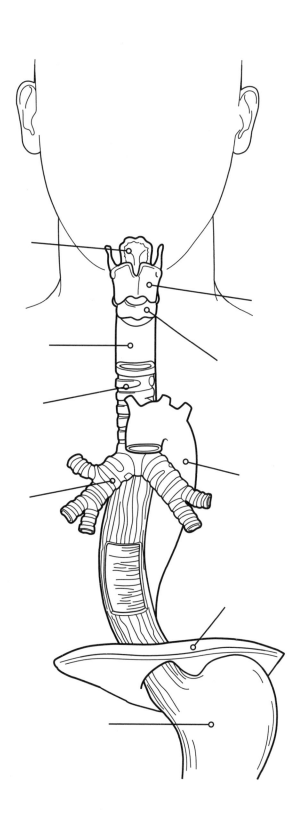

Blood vessels and nerves of the esophagus

The arterial supply of the esophagus derives from branches of the aorta and subclavian artery. As with much of the body, the veins that drain blood from the esophagus tend to run alongside the arteries.

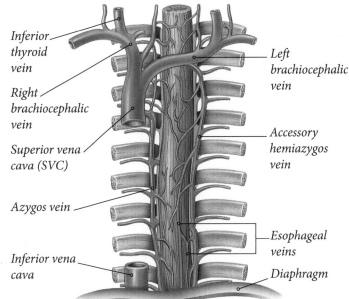

Inferior thyroid vein

Right brachiocephalic vein

Superior vena cava (SVC)

Azygos vein

Inferior vena cava

Left brachiocephalic vein

Accessory hemiazygos vein

Esophageal veins

Diaphragm

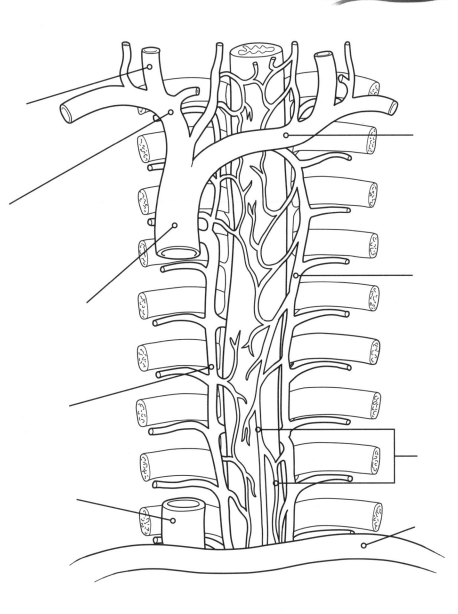

Stomach

The stomach is the expanded part of the digestive tract that receives swallowed food from the esophagus. Food is stored here before being propelled into the small intestine as digestion continues.

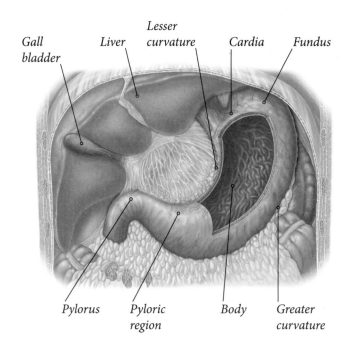

Gall bladder

Liver

Lesser curvature

Cardia

Fundus

Pylorus

Pyloric region

Body

Greater curvature

Blood supply of the stomach

The stomach has a profuse
blood supply, which comes
from the various branches of
the coeliac trunk.

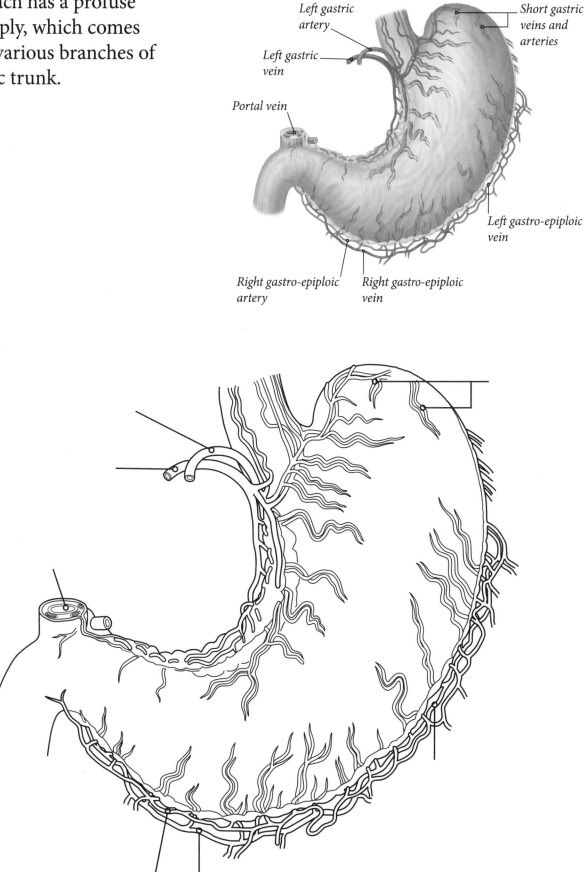

Left gastric
artery

Left gastric
vein

Portal vein

Short gastric
veins and
arteries

Left gastro-epiploic
vein

Right gastro-epiploic
artery

Right gastro-epiploic
vein

Small intestine

The small intestine extends from the stomach to the junction with the large intestine. It is made up of three parts and is the main site in the body where food is digested and absorbed.

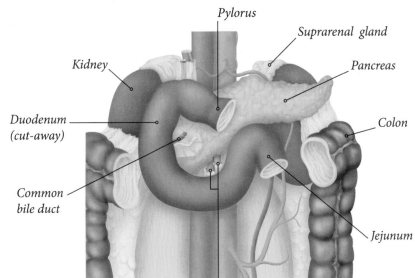

Pylorus

Suprarenal gland

Kidney

Pancreas

Duodenum (cut-away)

Colon

Common bile duct

Jejunum

Superior mesenteric artery and vein

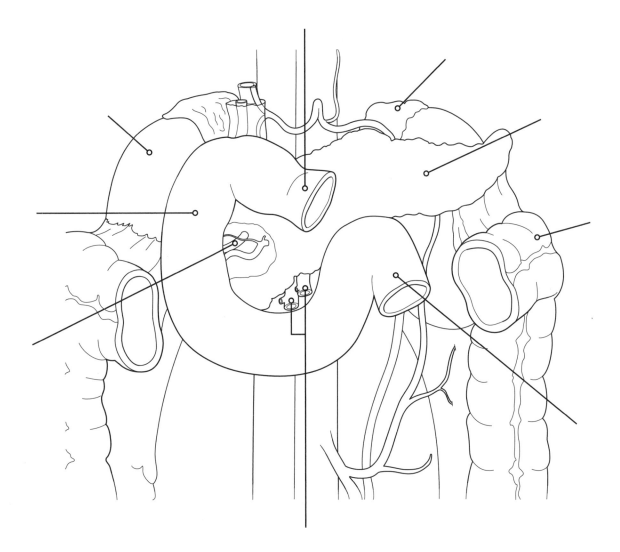

Jejunum and ileum

The jejunum and the ileum together form the longest part of the small intestine. Unlike the duodenum, they are able to move within the abdomen.

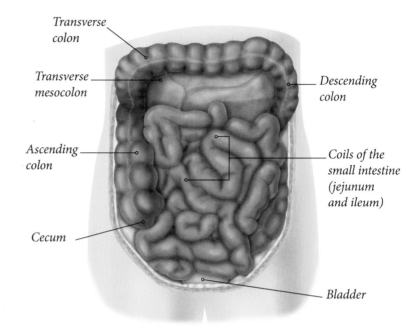

Transverse colon

Transverse mesocolon

Ascending colon

Cecum

Descending colon

Coils of the small intestine (jejunum and ileum)

Bladder

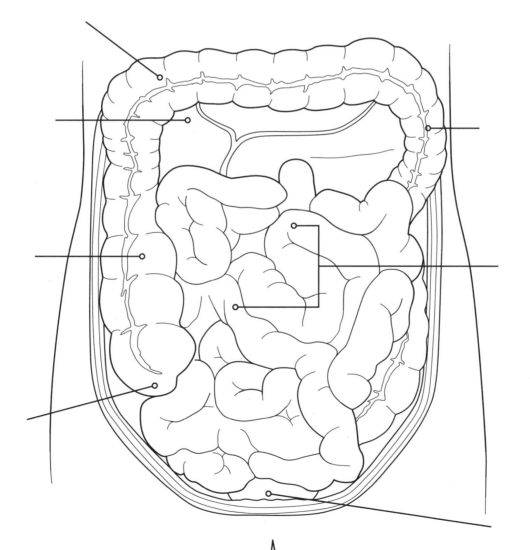

Liver

The liver is the largest abdominal organ, weighing about 3.3 pounds (1.5 kg) in adult men. It plays an important role in digestion, and also produces bile, which is secreted into the duodenum.

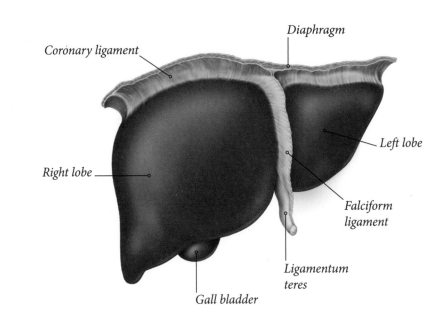

Coronary ligament

Diaphragm

Left lobe

Right lobe

Falciform ligament

Ligamentum teres

Gall bladder

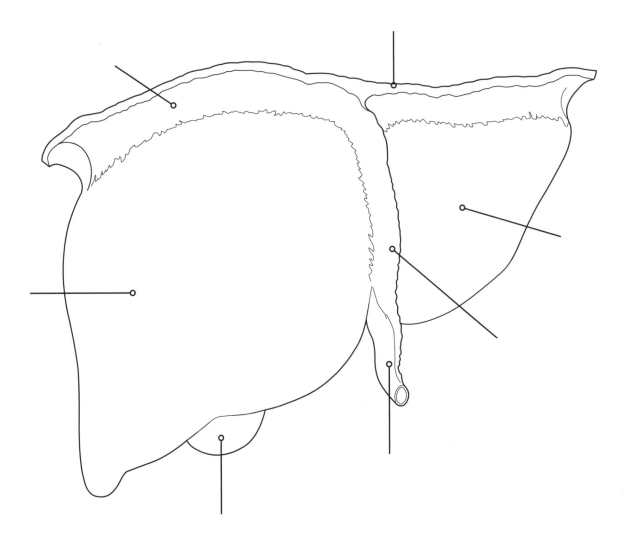

Visceral surface of the liver

The underside of the liver is known as the visceral surface as it lies against the abdominal organs, or viscera. The impressions of adjacent organs, the related vessels and the positions of the inferior vena cava and gall bladder can be seen.

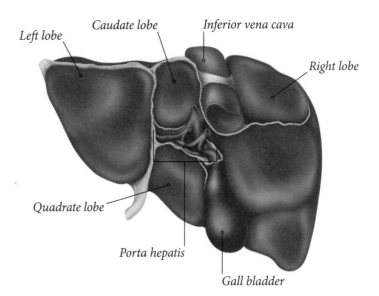

Left lobe

Caudate lobe

Inferior vena cava

Right lobe

Quadrate lobe

Porta hepatis

Gall bladder

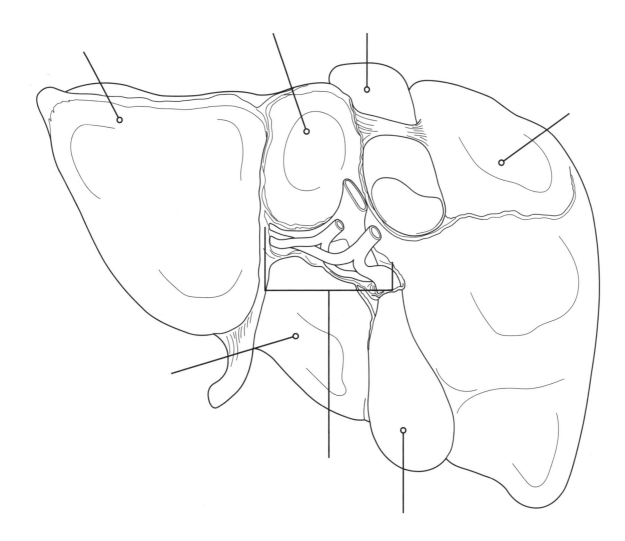

Cecum

The cecum and appendix lie at the junction of the large and small intestine, an area also known as the ileocecal region. The cecum, from which the appendix arises, receives food from the small intestine.

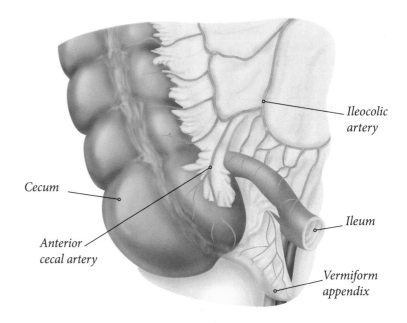

Cecum

Anterior cecal artery

Ileocolic artery

Ileum

Vermiform appendix

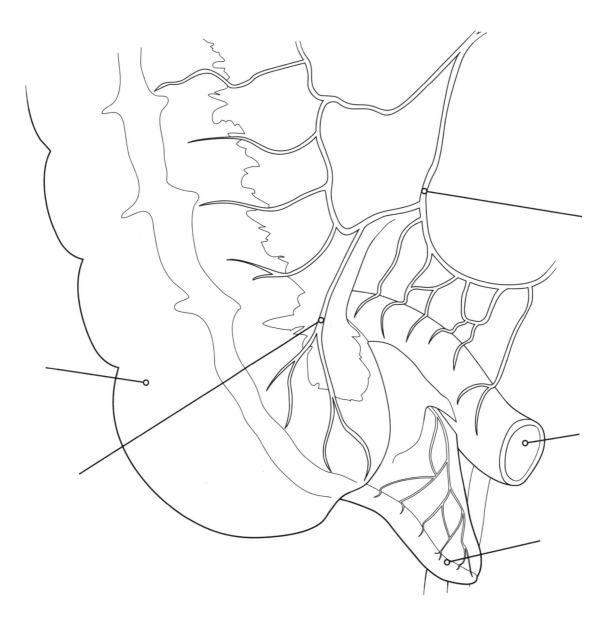

Appendix

The appendix is a narrow, muscular outpouching of the cecum. It is usually between 2 and 4 inches (6 and 10 cm) in length, although it may be much longer or shorter. It arises from the back of the cecum, its lower end being free and mobile.

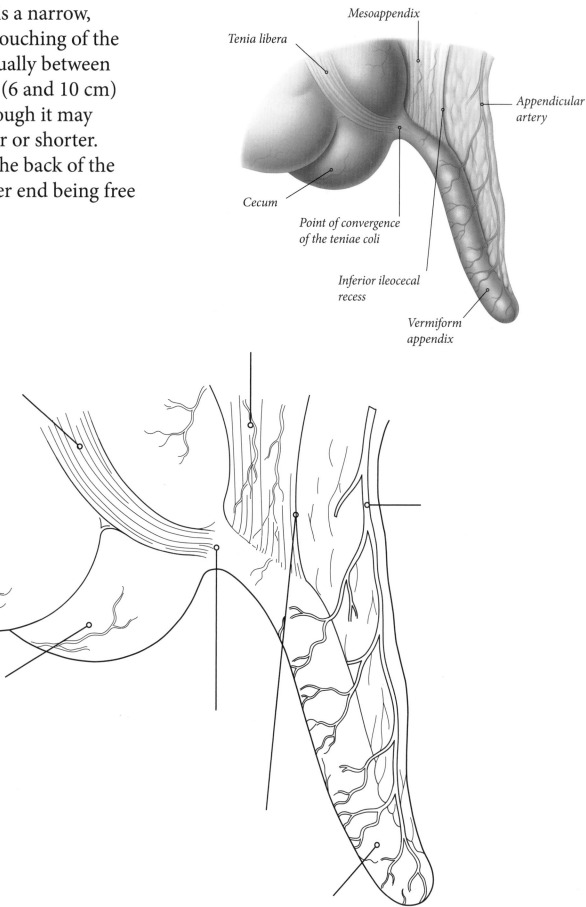

Mesoappendix

Tenia libera

Appendicular artery

Cecum

Point of convergence of the teniae coli

Inferior ileocecal recess

Vermiform appendix

Colon

The colon forms the main part of the large intestine. Although a continuous tube, the colon has four parts: the ascending colon, the transverse colon, the descending colon, and the sigmoid colon.

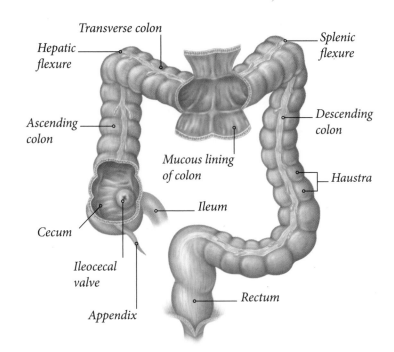

Transverse colon

Hepatic flexure

Splenic flexure

Ascending colon

Descending colon

Mucous lining of colon

Haustra

Cecum

Ileum

Ileocecal valve

Rectum

Appendix

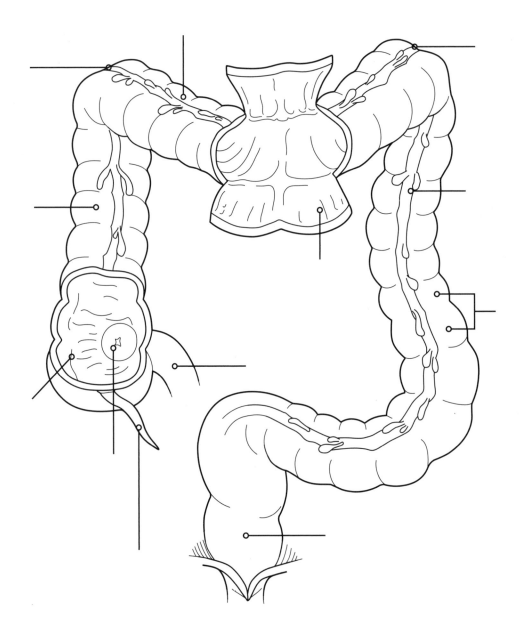

Blood supply and drainage of the colon

Like the rest of the intestine, each of the parts of the colon is readily supplied with blood from a network of arteries.

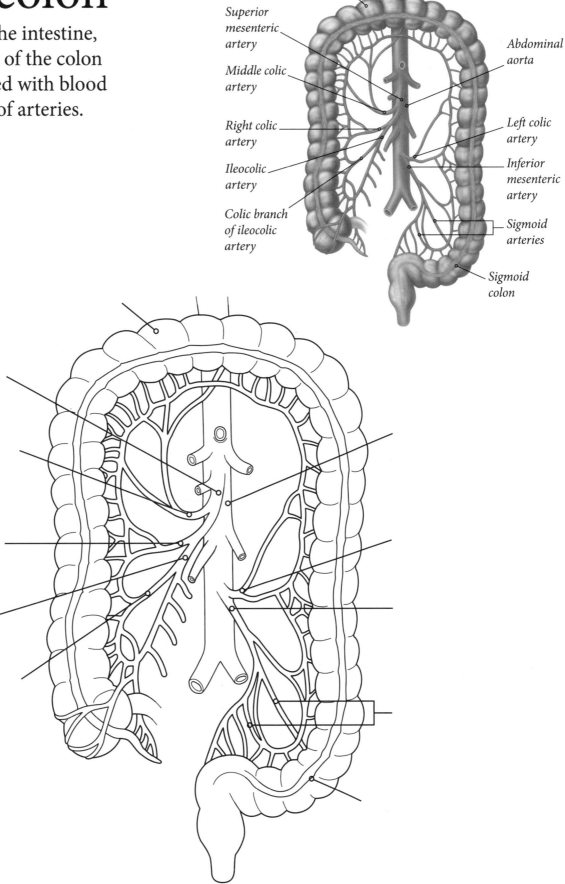

Transverse colon

Superior mesenteric artery

Middle colic artery

Right colic artery

Ileocolic artery

Colic branch of ileocolic artery

Abdominal aorta

Left colic artery

Inferior mesenteric artery

Sigmoid arteries

Sigmoid colon

Rectum and anal canal

The rectum and anal canal together form the last part of the gastro-intestinal tract. They receive waste matter in the form of feces and allow it to be passed out of the body.

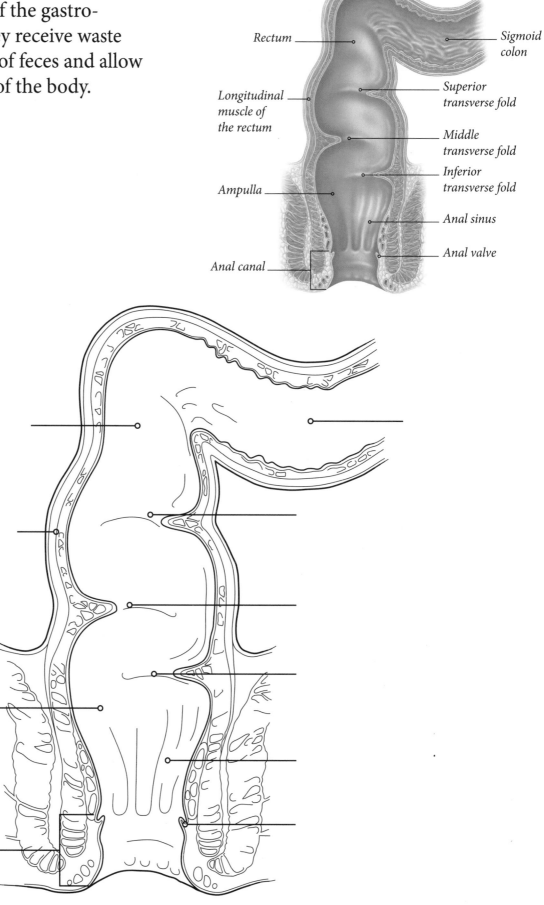

Rectum

Sigmoid colon

Longitudinal muscle of the rectum

Superior transverse fold

Middle transverse fold

Inferior transverse fold

Ampulla

Anal sinus

Anal valve

Anal canal

Vessels of the rectum and anus

The rectum and anal canal have a
rich blood supply. A network of
veins drains blood from this area.

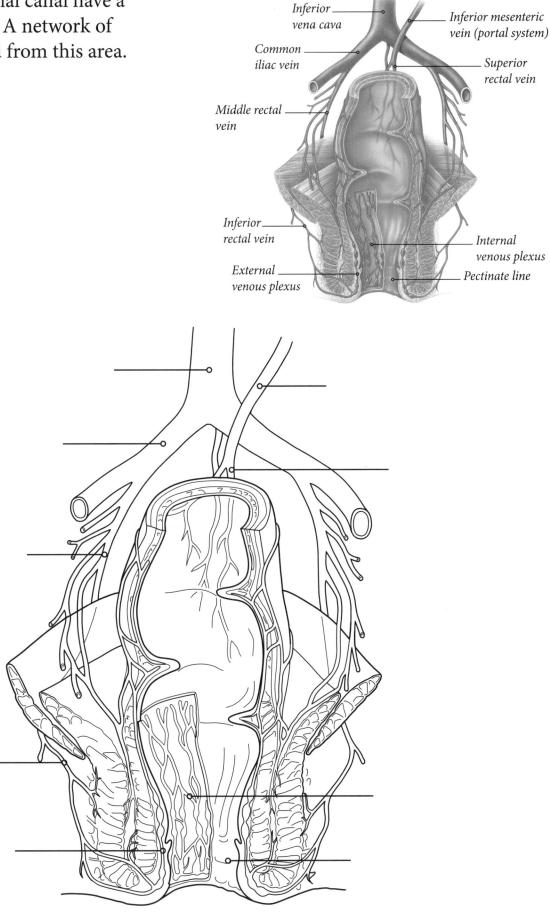

Inferior
vena cava

Inferior mesenteric
vein (portal system)

Common
iliac vein

Superior
rectal vein

Middle rectal
vein

Inferior
rectal vein

Internal
venous plexus

External
venous plexus

Pectinate line

Pancreas

The pancreas is a large gland that produces both enzymes and hormones. It lies in the upper abdomen behind the stomach, one end in the curve of the duodenum and the other end touching the spleen.

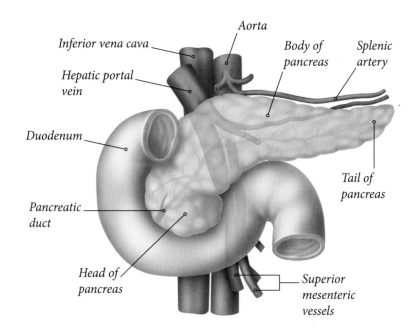

Inferior vena cava

Hepatic portal vein

Duodenum

Pancreatic duct

Head of pancreas

Aorta

Body of pancreas

Splenic artery

Tail of pancreas

Superior mesenteric vessels

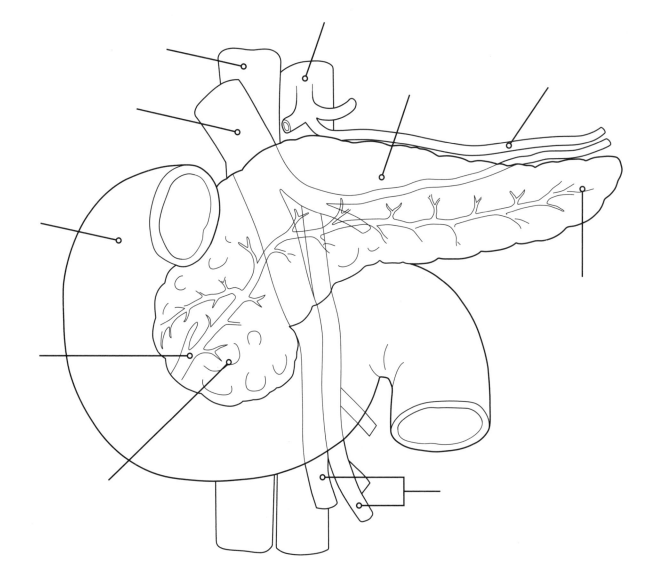

The spleen

The spleen is the largest of the lymphatic organs. It is dark purple in color and lies under the lower ribs on the left side of the upper abdomen.

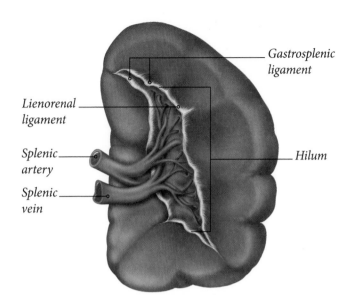

Gastrosplenic ligament

Lienorenal ligament

Splenic artery

Splenic vein

Hilum

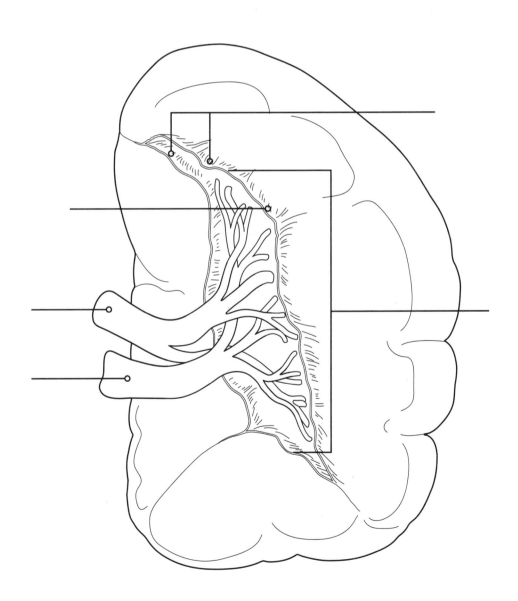

Inguinal region

The inguinal region, commonly known as the groin, is the site of inguinal hernias. The abdominal wall has an area of weakness, which may allow the abdominal contents to protrude through it.

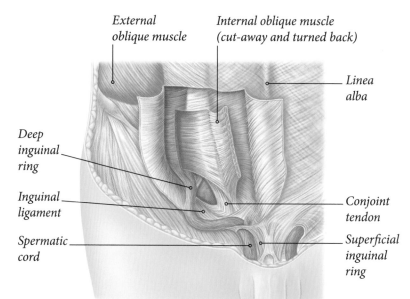

External oblique muscle

Internal oblique muscle (cut-away and turned back)

Linea alba

Deep inguinal ring

Inguinal ligament

Spermatic cord

Conjoint tendon

Superficial inguinal ring

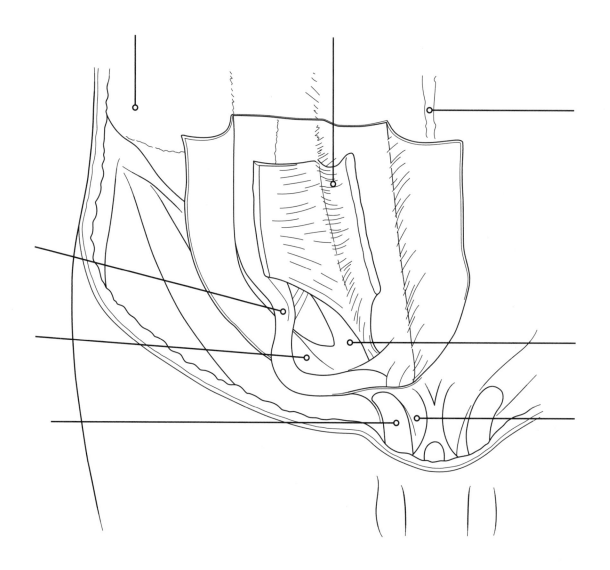

Overview of the urinary tract

The urinary tract consists of the kidneys, ureters, urinary bladder, and urethra. Together, these organs are responsible for the production of urine and its expulsion from the body.

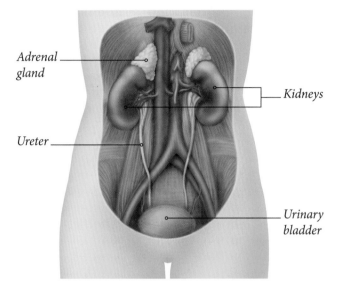

Adrenal gland

Ureter

Kidneys

Urinary bladder

ANTERIOR VIEW

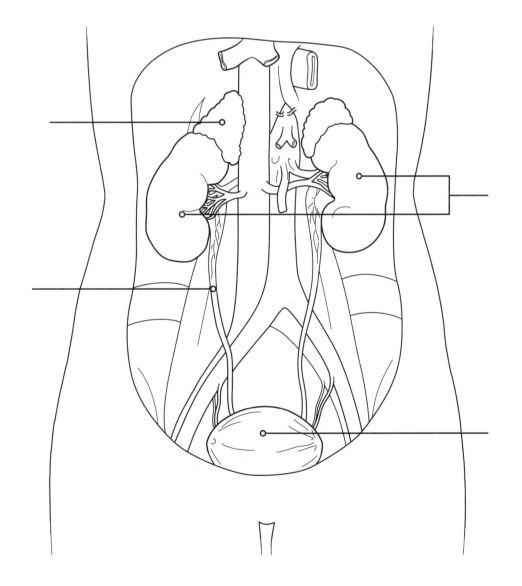

Adrenal glands

The adrenal glands are situated above the kidneys, but are not part of the urinary tract. Each one consists of two separate parts: a medulla surrounded by a cortex.

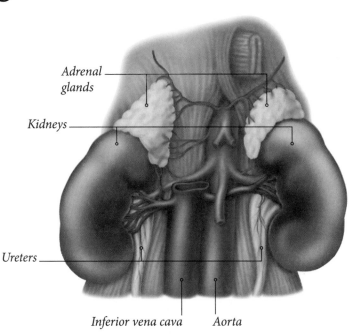

Adrenal glands

Kidneys

Ureters

Inferior vena cava   Aorta

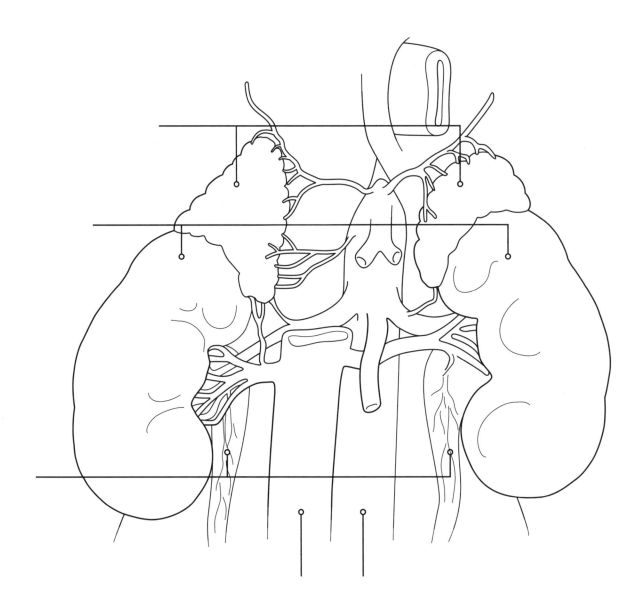

Kidneys

The kidneys are a pair of solid organs situated at the back of the abdomen. They act as filtering units for blood and maintain the balance and composition of fluids within the body.

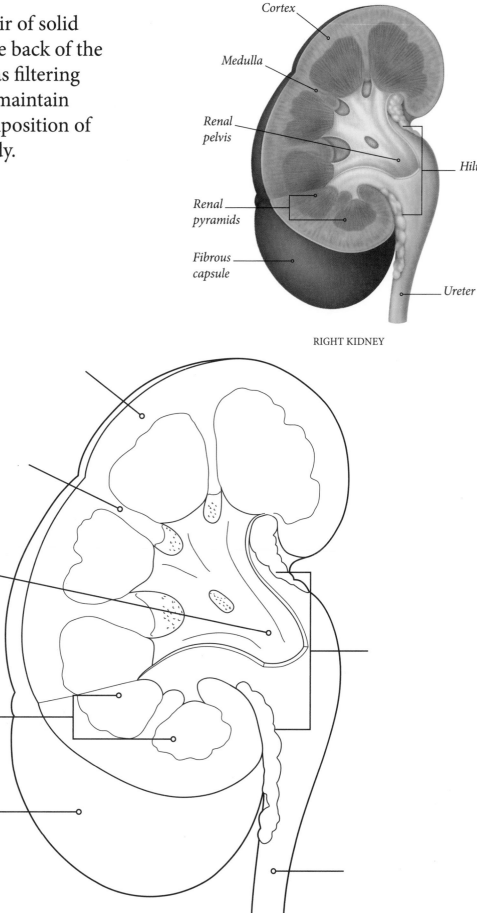

Cortex

Medulla

Renal pelvis

Hilus

Renal pyramids

Fibrous capsule

Ureter

RIGHT KIDNEY

Blood supply to the kidneys

The function of the kidneys is to filter blood, for which they receive an exceedingly rich blood supply. As with other parts of the body, the pattern of drainage of venous blood mirrors the pattern of arterial supply.

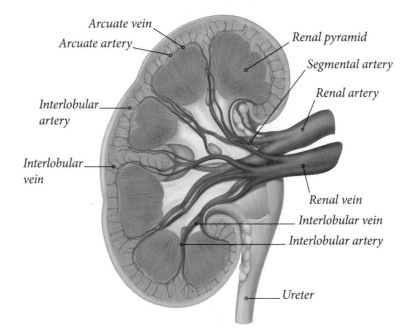

Arcuate vein

Arcuate artery

Renal pyramid

Segmental artery

Renal artery

Interlobular artery

Interlobular vein

Renal vein

Interlobular vein

Interlobular artery

Ureter

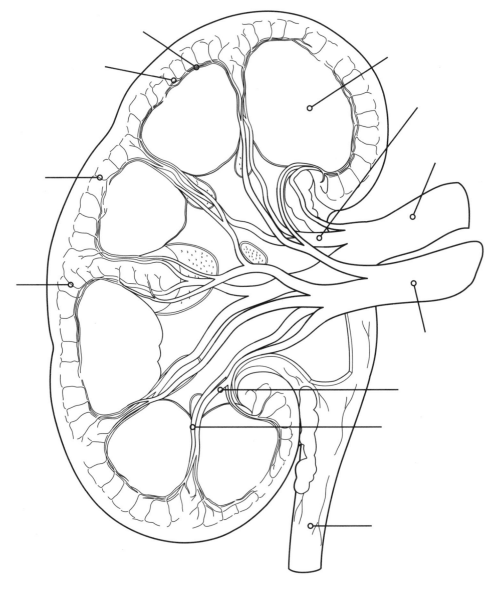

Bladder

The ureters channel urine produced by the kidneys down their length and into the urinary bladder. Urine is stored in the bladder until it is expelled from the body via the urethra.

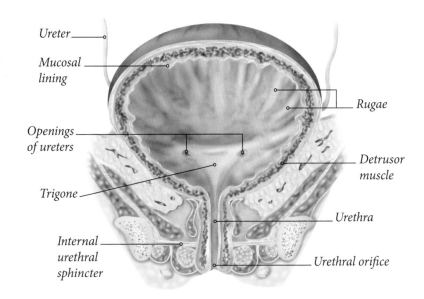

Ureter

Mucosal lining

Openings of ureters

Trigone

Internal urethral sphincter

Rugae

Detrusor muscle

Urethra

Urethral orifice

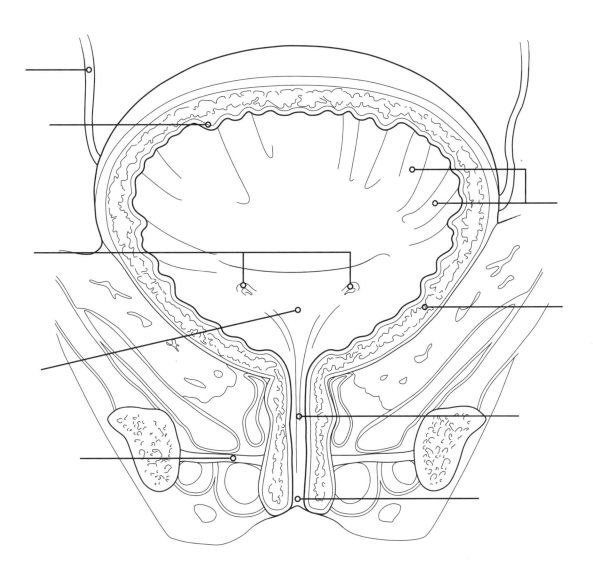

Ureters

The ureters are tubular and propel the urine toward the bladder. Each ureter squeezes and contracts its muscles to encourage the free flow of urine.

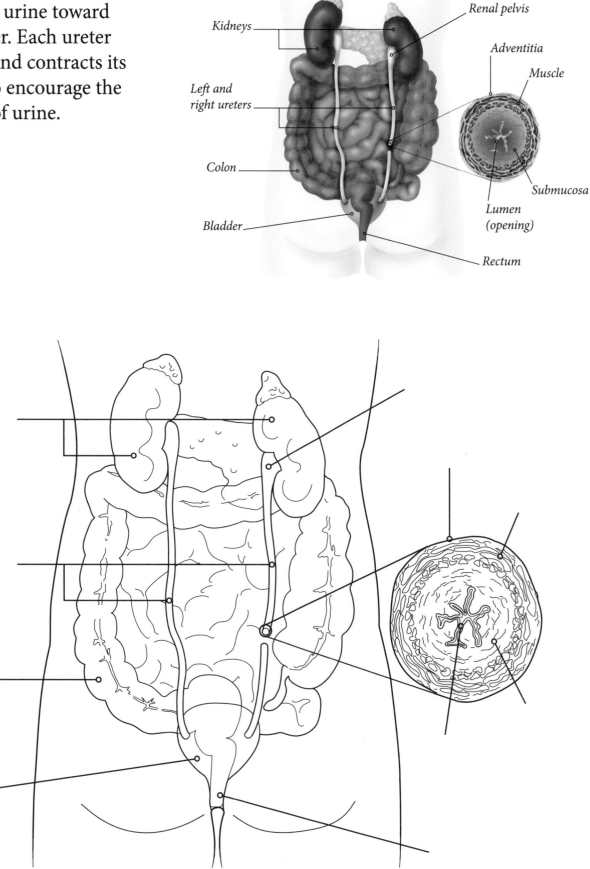

Kidneys

Renal pelvis

Adventitia

Muscle

Left and right ureters

Colon

Submucosa

Lumen (opening)

Bladder

Rectum

Male reproductive system

The male reproductive system includes the penis, scrotum, and the two testes (contained within the scrotum). The internal structures of the reproductive system are contained within the pelvis.

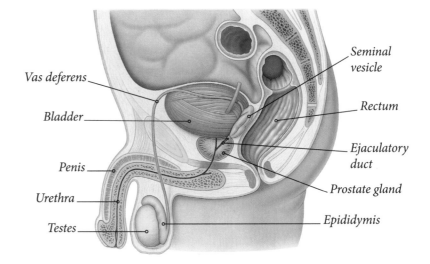

Vas deferens

Bladder

Penis

Urethra

Testes

Seminal vesicle

Rectum

Ejaculatory duct

Prostate gland

Epididymis

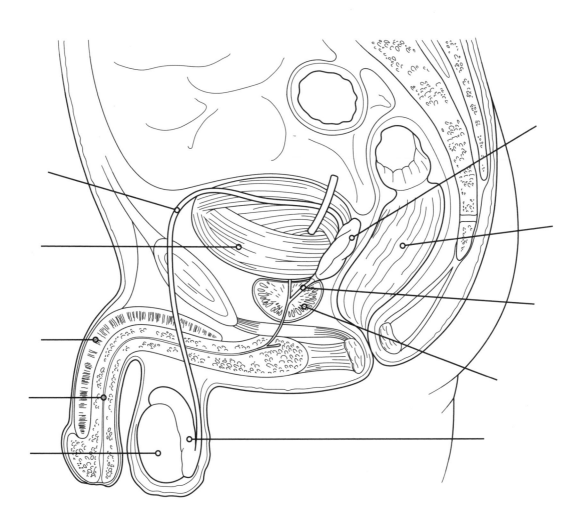

Prostate gland

The prostate gland forms
a vital part of the male
reproductive system,
providing enzyme-rich
fluid, and produces up
to a third of the total
volume of the seminal
fluid.

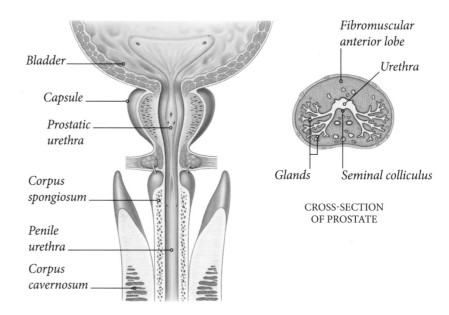

Bladder

Capsule

Prostatic
urethra

Corpus
spongiosum

Penile
urethra

Corpus
cavernosum

Fibromuscular
anterior lobe

Urethra

Glands

Seminal colliculus

CROSS-SECTION
OF PROSTATE

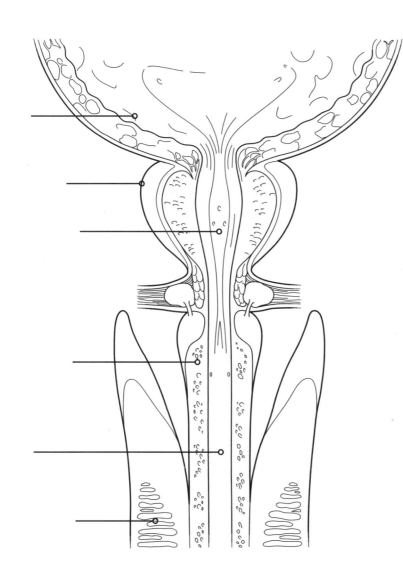

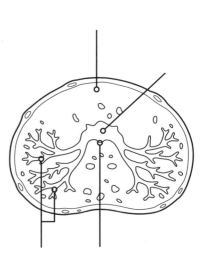

Testes, scrotum, and epididymis

The testes, which lie suspended within the scrotum, are the sites of sperm production. The scrotum also contains the two epididymides—long, coiled tubes, which connect to the vas deferens.

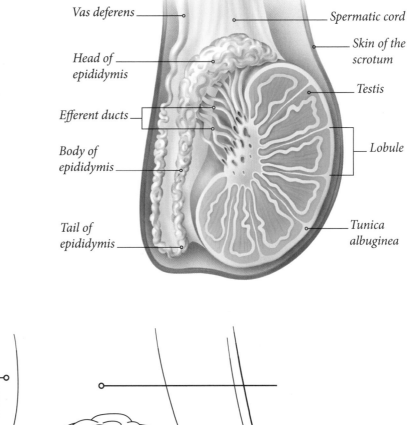

Vas deferens

Spermatic cord

Skin of the scrotum

Head of epididymis

Testis

Efferent ducts

Lobule

Body of epididymis

Tail of epididymis

Tunica albuginea

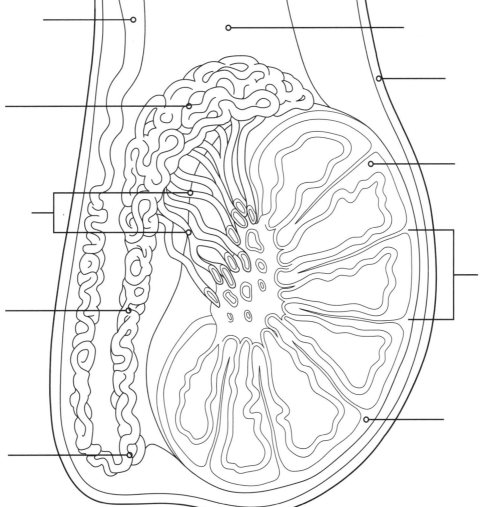

Blood supply of the testes

The arterial blood supply
of the testes arises from the
abdominal aorta, and descends
to the scrotum. Venous
drainage follows the same
route in reverse.

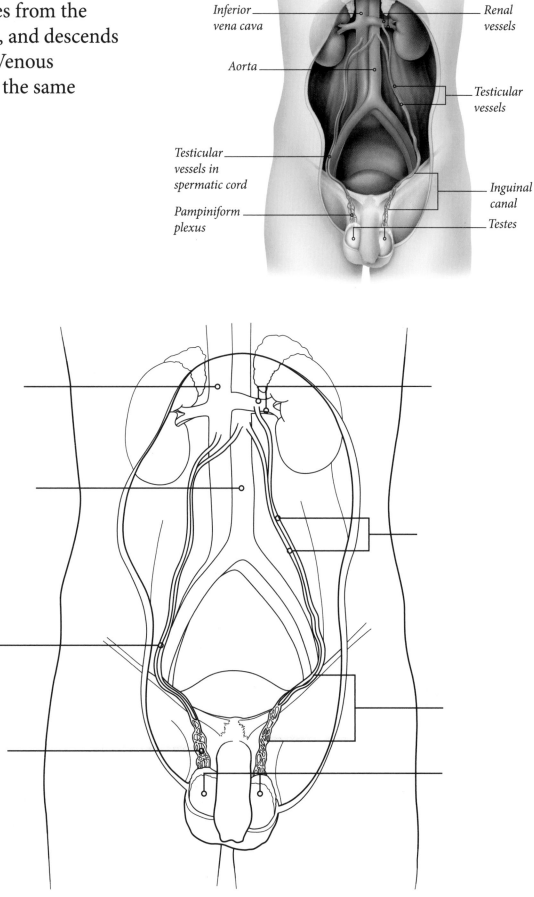

Inferior vena cava

Renal vessels

Aorta

Testicular vessels

Testicular vessels in spermatic cord

Inguinal canal

Pampiniform plexus

Testes

Penis

The penis is the male copulatory organ, which, when erect, conveys sperm into the vagina during sexual intercourse. To enable this, the penis is largely composed of erectile tissue.

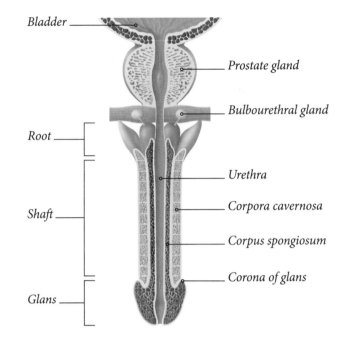

Bladder

Prostate gland

Bulbourethral gland

Root

Shaft

Glans

Urethra

Corpora cavernosa

Corpus spongiosum

Corona of glans

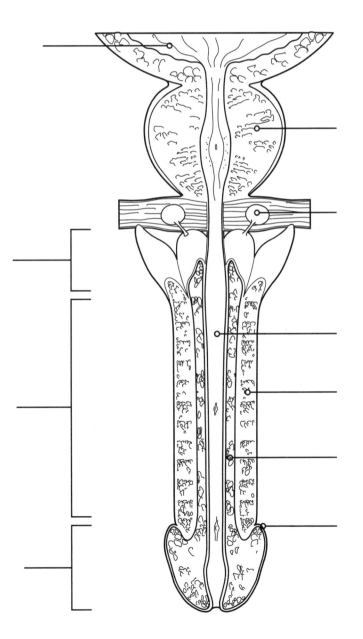

Muscles associated with the penis

Several muscles are associated with the penis. Their fibers are confined to the root and structures around the penis, rather than to the shaft or glans.

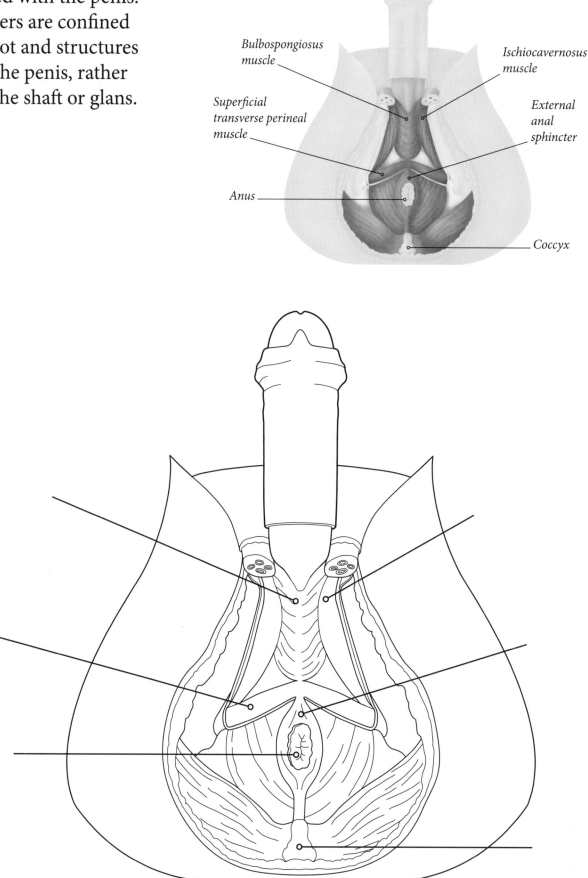

Bulbospongiosus muscle

Ischiocavernosus muscle

Superficial transverse perineal muscle

External anal sphincter

Anus

Coccyx

Female reproductive system

The role of the female reproductive tract is twofold. The ovaries produce eggs for fertilization, and the uterus nurtures and protects any resulting fetus for its nine-month gestation.

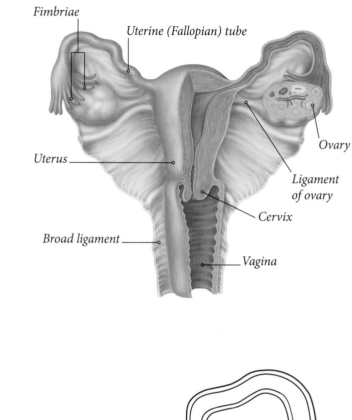

Fimbriae

Uterine (Fallopian) tube

Uterus

Ovary

Ligament of ovary

Cervix

Broad ligament

Vagina

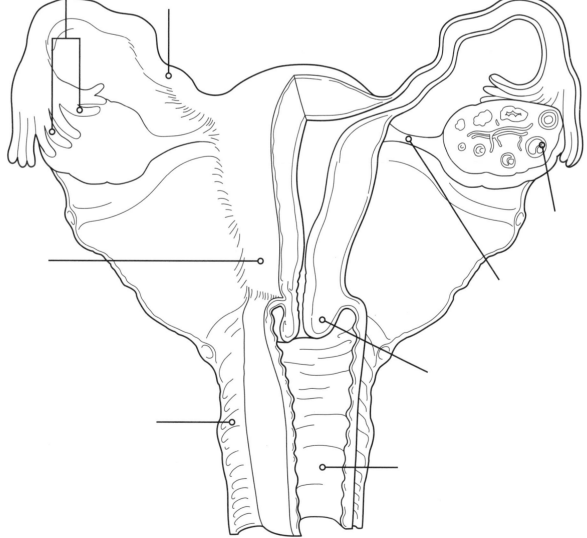

Blood supply of the internal genitalia

The female reproductive tract receives a rich blood supply via an interconnecting network of arteries. Venous blood is drained by a network of veins.

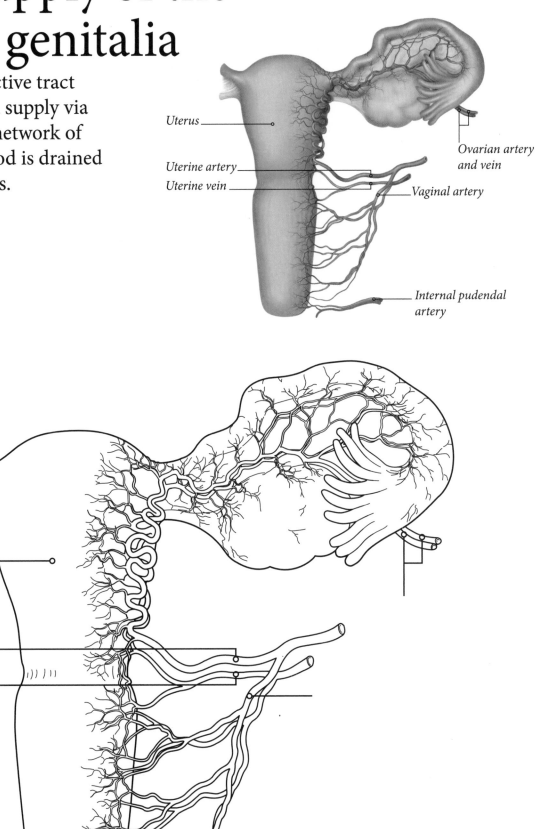

Uterus

Uterine artery

Uterine vein

Ovarian artery and vein

Vaginal artery

Internal pudendal artery

Uterus

The uterus, or womb, is the part of the female reproductive tract that nurtures and protects the fetus during pregnancy. It lies within the pelvic cavity and is a hollow, muscular organ.

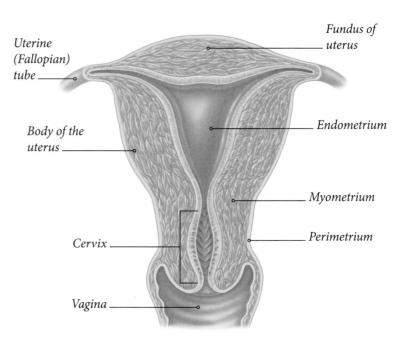

Uterine (Fallopian) tube

Fundus of uterus

Body of the uterus

Endometrium

Myometrium

Perimetrium

Cervix

Vagina

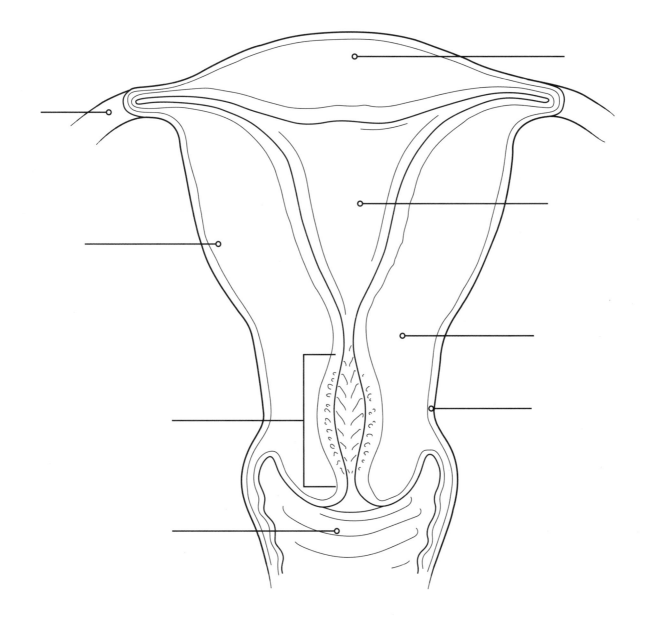

The uterus in pregnancy

In pregnancy the uterus must enlarge to hold the growing fetus. From being a small pelvic organ, it increases in size to take up much of the space of the abdominal cavity.

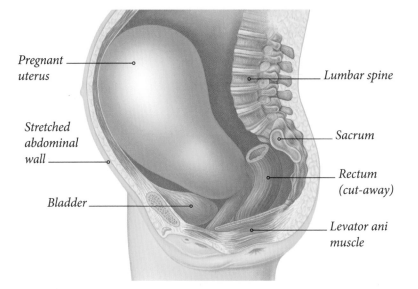

Pregnant uterus

Lumbar spine

Stretched abdominal wall

Sacrum

Rectum (cut-away)

Bladder

Levator ani muscle

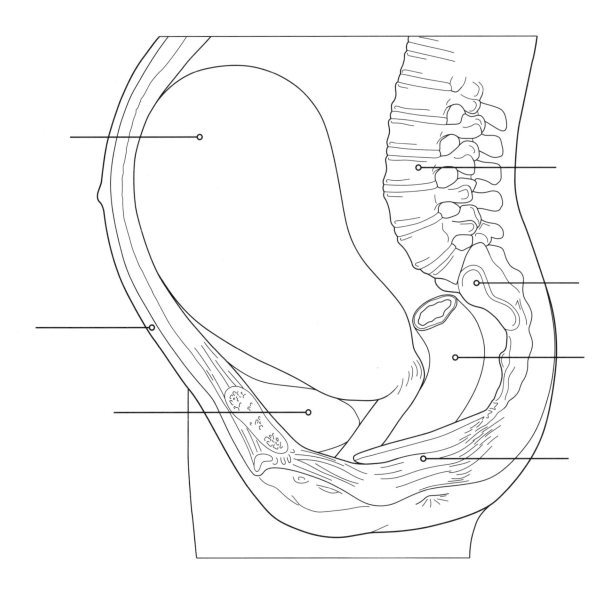

Vagina

The vagina is the thin-walled muscular tube that extends from the cervix of the uterus to the external genitalia. The vagina is closed at rest but is designed to stretch during intercourse or childbirth.

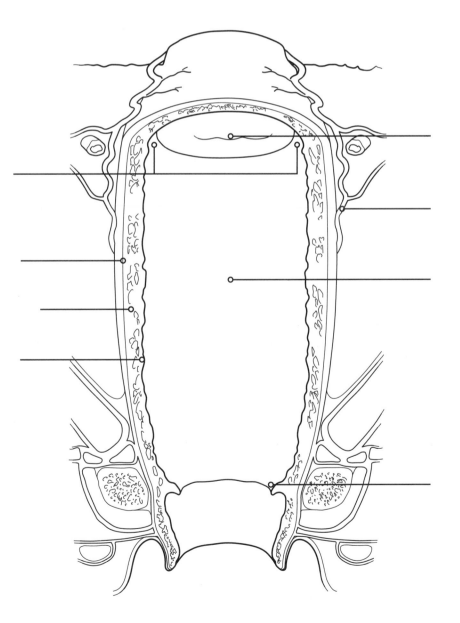

Vaginal fornices

Cervical os

Vaginal artery

Adventitia

Vaginal lumen

Muscle layer

Mucosa

Hymenal caruncle

Cervix

The cervix, or neck of the uterus, is the narrowed, lower part of the uterus which projects down into the upper vagina.

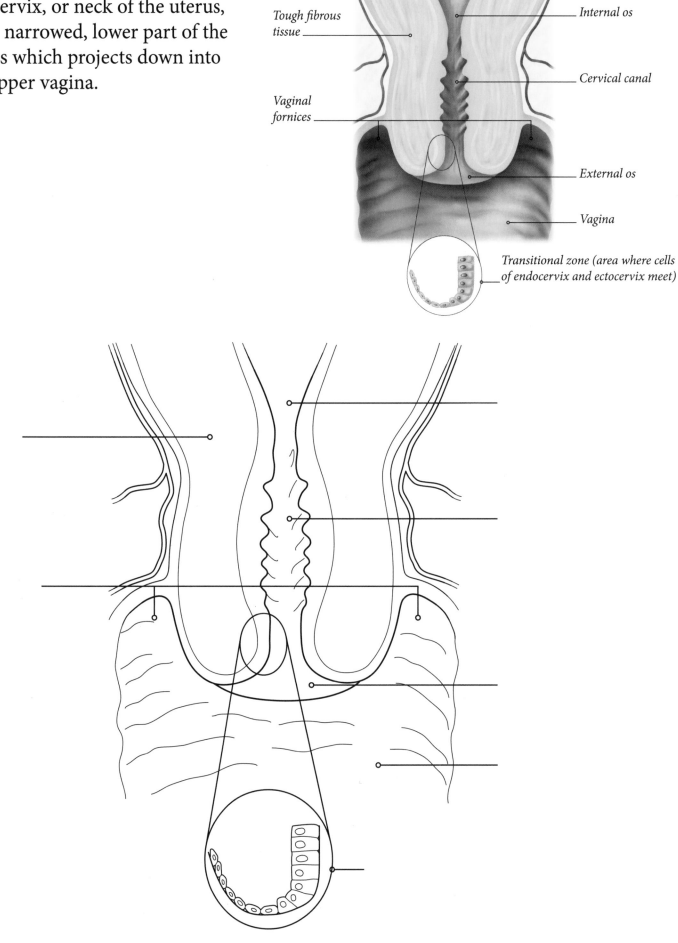

Tough fibrous tissue

Internal os

Cervical canal

Vaginal fornices

External os

Vagina

Transitional zone (area where cells of endocervix and ectocervix meet)

Ovaries

The ovaries are the site of production of oocytes, or eggs, which are fertilized by sperm to produce embryos. The uterine (or Fallopian) tubes conduct the oocytes from the ovaries to the uterus.

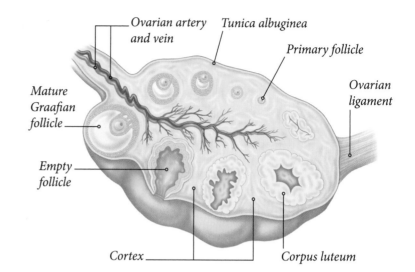

Ovarian artery and vein Tunica albuginea Primary follicle

Ovarian ligament

Mature Graafian follicle

Empty follicle

Cortex Corpus luteum

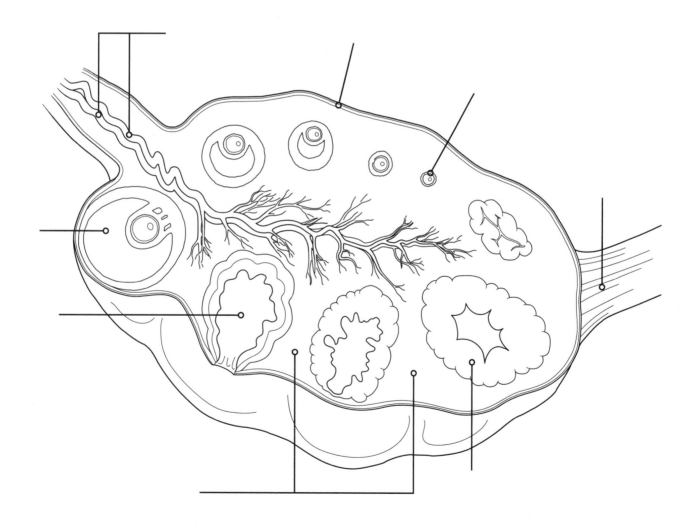

Uterine tubes

The uterine, or Fallopian, tubes collect the oocytes released from the ovaries and transport them to the uterus. They also provide a site for fertilization of the oocyte by a sperm to take place.

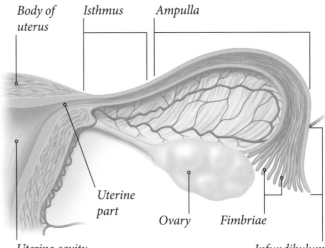

Body of uterus

Isthmus

Ampulla

Uterine part

Uterine cavity

Ovary

Fimbriae

Infundibulum

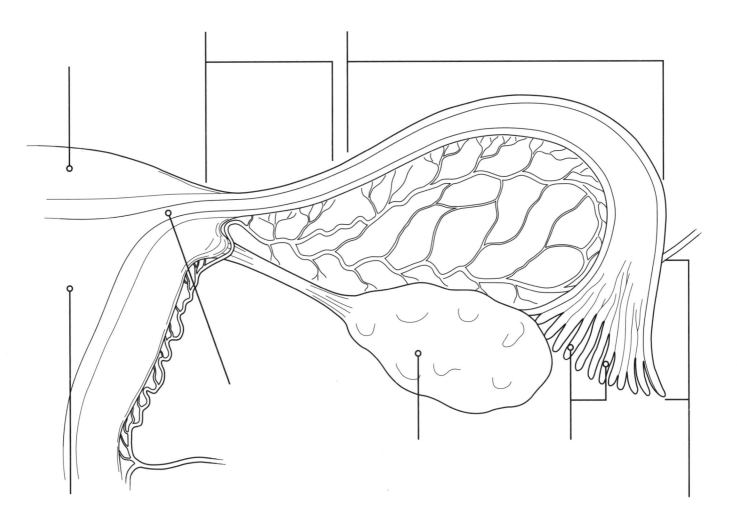

Bones of the pelvis

The basin-like pelvis is formed by the hip bones, sacrum and coccyx. The pelvic bones provide sites of attachment for many important muscles, and also help to protect the vital pelvic organs.

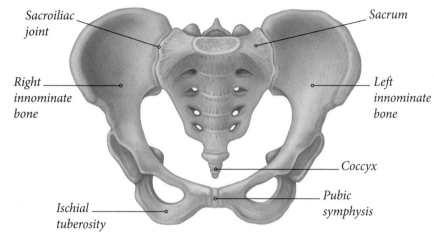

Sacroiliac joint

Sacrum

Right innominate bone

Left innominate bone

Coccyx

Pubic symphysis

Ischial tuberosity

ADULT FEMALE PELVIS

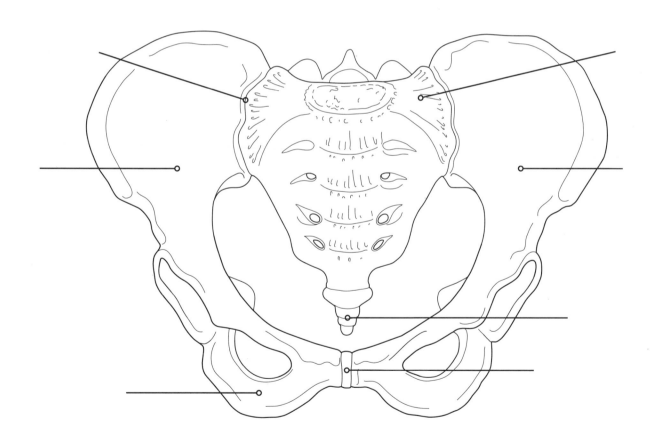

Hip bone

The two hip bones are fused together at the front and join with the sacrum at the back. They each consist of three bones—the ilium, ischium, and pubis.

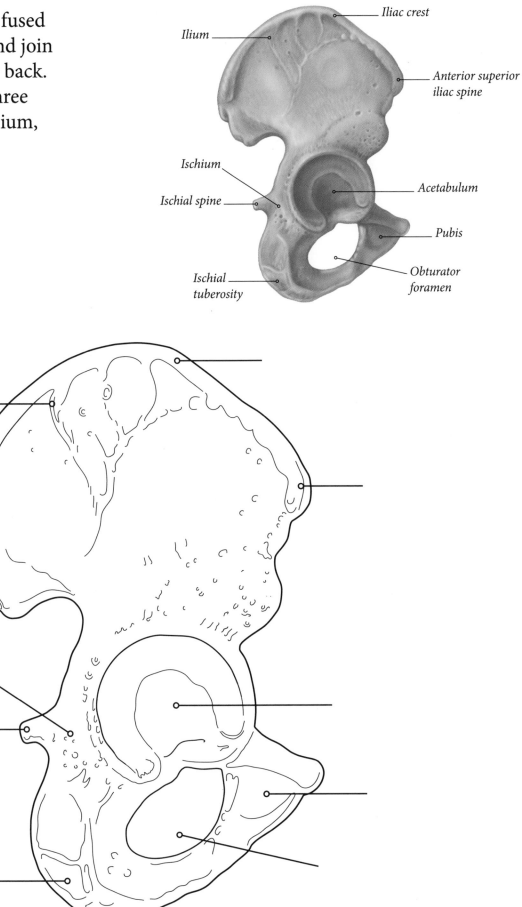

Iliac crest

Ilium

Anterior superior iliac spine

Ischium

Acetabulum

Ischial spine

Pubis

Obturator foramen

Ischial tuberosity

Pelvic floor muscles

The muscles of the pelvic floor play a vital role in supporting the abdominal and pelvic organs. They also help to regulate the processes of defecation and urination.

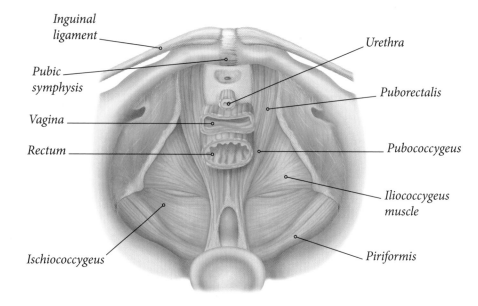

Inguinal ligament

Pubic symphysis

Vagina

Rectum

Ischiococcygeus

Urethra

Puborectalis

Pubococcygeus

Iliococcygeus muscle

Piriformis

FEMALE PELVIC DIAPHRAGM FROM ABOVE

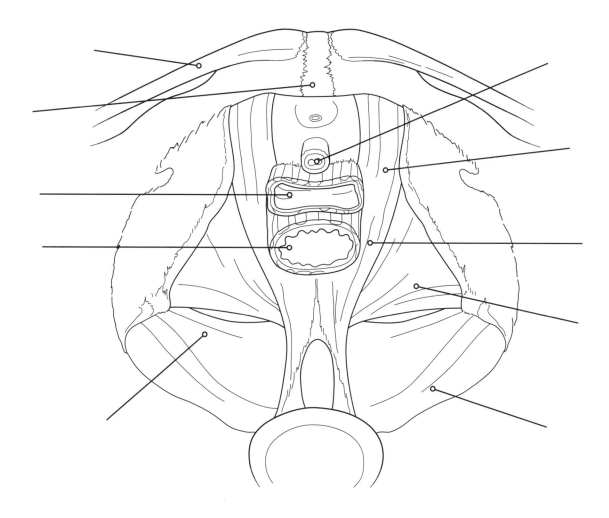

Openings of the pelvic floor

The pelvic floor resembles the diaphragm in the chest in that it forms a nearly continuous sheet, but does have openings to allow important structures to pass through it. There are two important openings situated in the pelvic floor region.

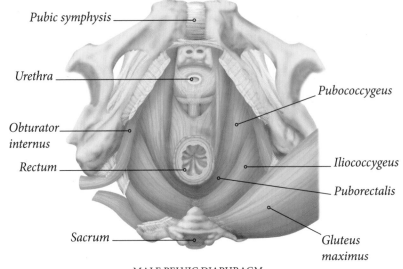

Pubic symphysis

Urethra

Obturator internus

Rectum

Sacrum

Pubococcygeus

Iliococcygeus

Puborectalis

Gluteus maximus

MALE PELVIC DIAPHRAGM
FROM BELOW

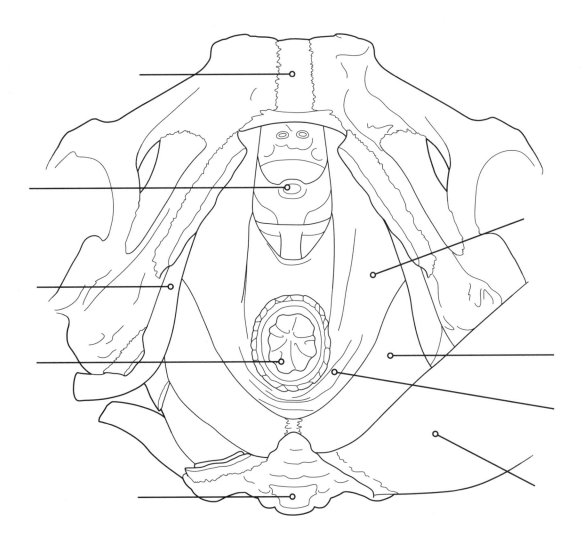

Muscles of the gluteal region

The gluteus maximus is the largest and heaviest of all the gluteal muscles and is situated in the buttock region. This strong, thick muscle plays an important part in enabling humans to stand.

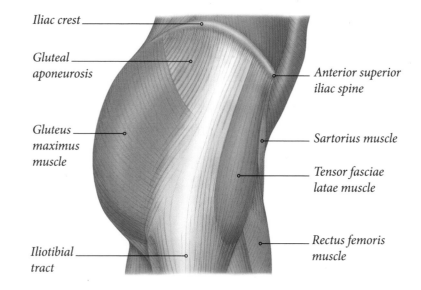

Iliac crest

Gluteal aponeurosis

Gluteus maximus muscle

Iliotibial tract

Anterior superior iliac spine

Sartorius muscle

Tensor fasciae latae muscle

Rectus femoris muscle

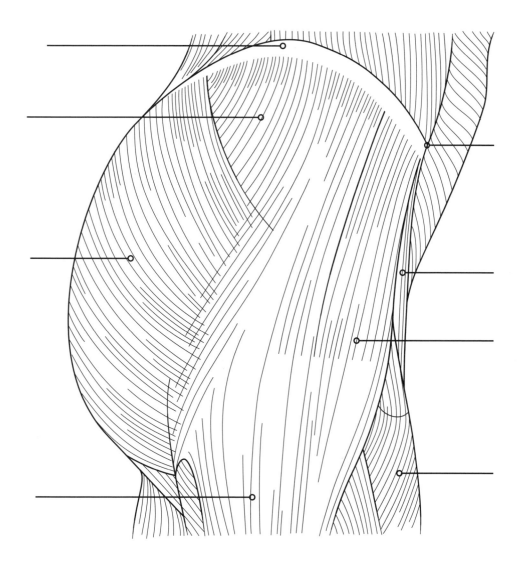

Hip joint

The hip joint is the strong ball-and-socket joint that connects the lower limb to the pelvis. Of all the body's joints, the hip is second only to the shoulder in the variety of movements it allows.

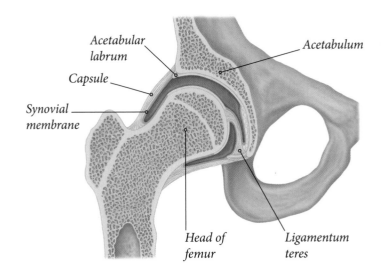

Acetabular labrum

Acetabulum

Capsule

Synovial membrane

Head of femur

Ligamentum teres

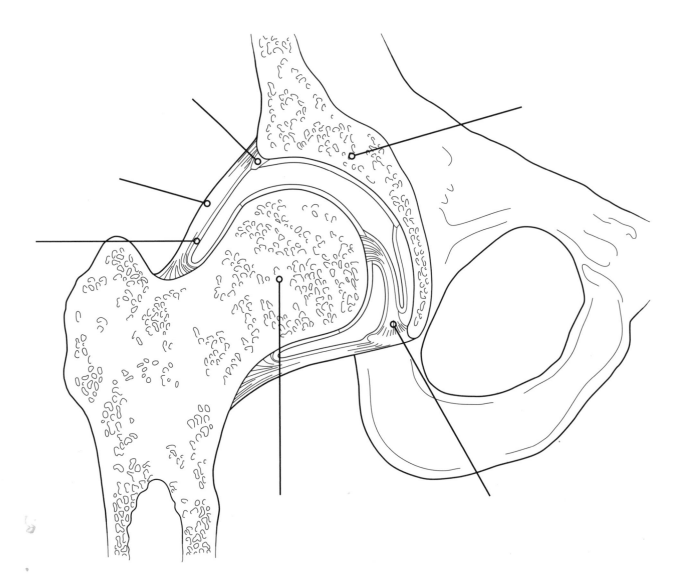

Ligaments of the hip joint

The hip joint is enclosed and protected by a thick, fibrous capsule. The capsule is flexible enough to allow the joint a wide range of movements but is strengthened by a number of tough ligaments.

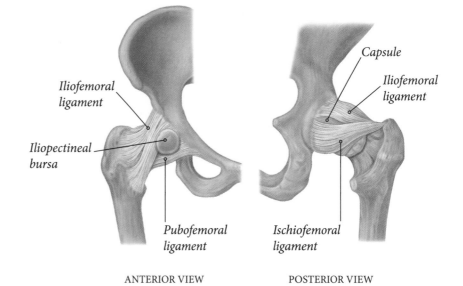

Iliofemoral ligament

Iliopectineal bursa

Pubofemoral ligament

Capsule

Iliofemoral ligament

Ischiofemoral ligament

ANTERIOR VIEW

POSTERIOR VIEW

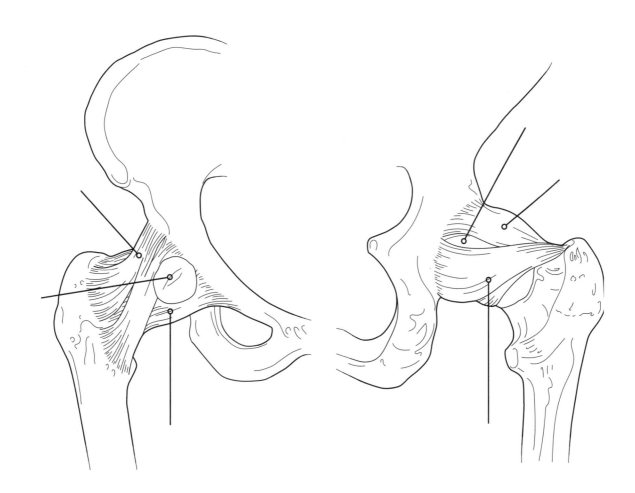

Femur

The femur, or thigh bone, is the longest and heaviest bone in the body. Measuring approximately 18 inches (45 cm) in length in adult males, the femur makes up about one quarter of a person's total height.

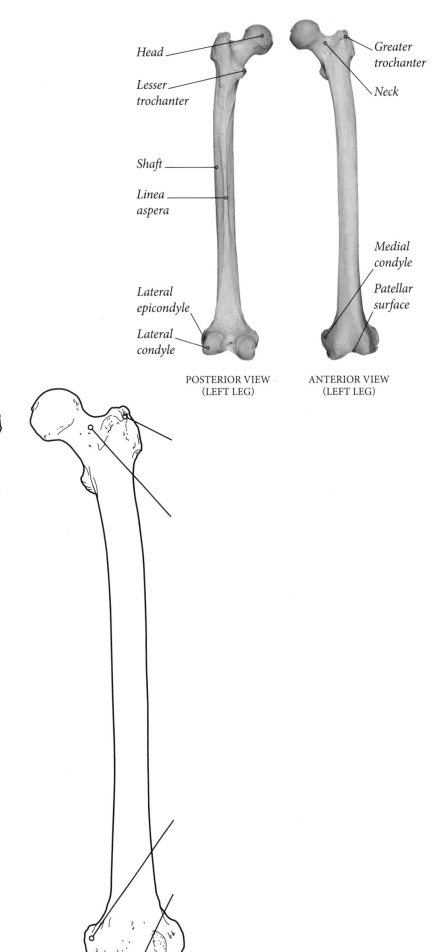

Head

Lesser trochanter

Shaft

Linea aspera

Lateral epicondyle

Lateral condyle

Greater trochanter

Neck

Medial condyle

Patellar surface

POSTERIOR VIEW
(LEFT LEG)

ANTERIOR VIEW
(LEFT LEG)

Muscle attachments of the femur

The femur is a very strong bone that provides sites of attachment for many of the muscles of locomotion in the hip joint and legs.

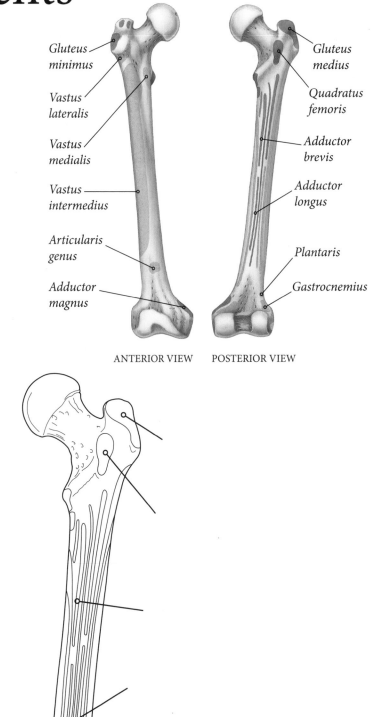

Gluteus minimus

Vastus lateralis

Vastus medialis

Vastus intermedius

Articularis genus

Adductor magnus

Gluteus medius

Quadratus femoris

Adductor brevis

Adductor longus

Plantaris

Gastrocnemius

ANTERIOR VIEW   POSTERIOR VIEW

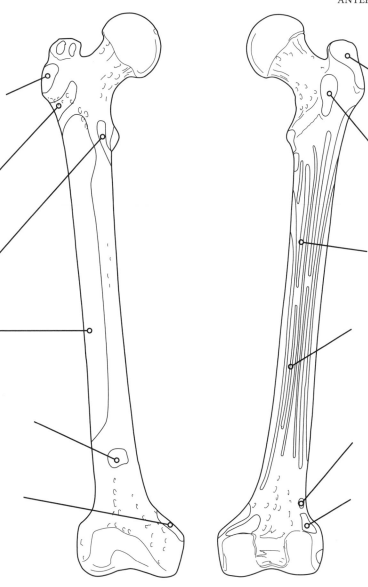

Tibia and fibula

The tibia and fibula together form the skeleton of the lower leg. The tibia is much larger and stronger than the fibula as it must bear the weight of the body.

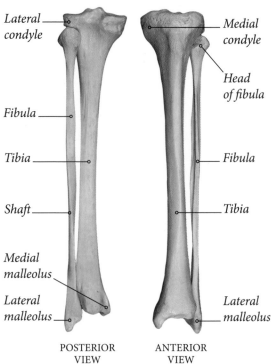

Lateral condyle

Medial condyle

Head of fibula

Fibula

Fibula

Tibia

Tibia

Shaft

Medial malleolus

Lateral malleolus

Lateral malleolus

POSTERIOR VIEW

ANTERIOR VIEW

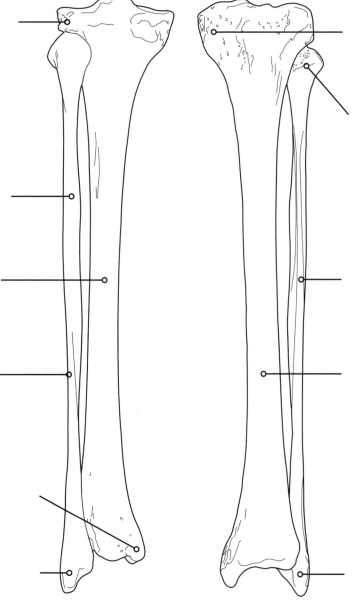

Ligaments of the tibia and fibula

The ligaments that surround the tibia and fibula bind the two bones to each other and to the other leg bones with which they articulate.

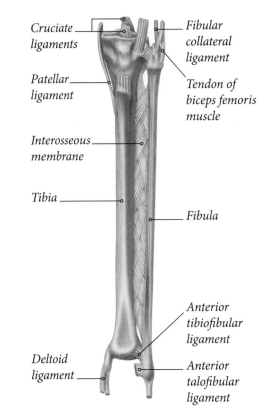

Cruciate ligaments

Patellar ligament

Interosseous membrane

Tibia

Deltoid ligament

Fibular collateral ligament

Tendon of biceps femoris muscle

Fibula

Anterior tibiofibular ligament

Anterior talofibular ligament

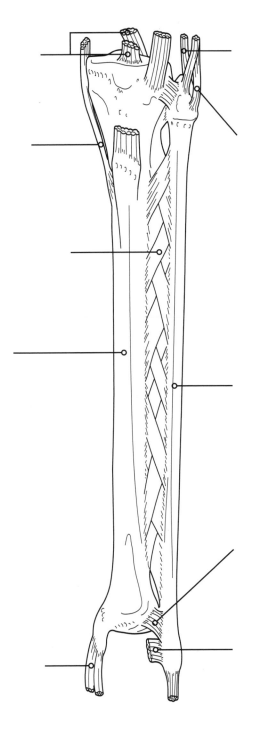

Knee joint and patella

The knee is the joint between
the end of the thigh bone and
the top of the tibia. In front of
the knee is the patella (kneecap),
the convex surface of which can
readily be felt under the skin.

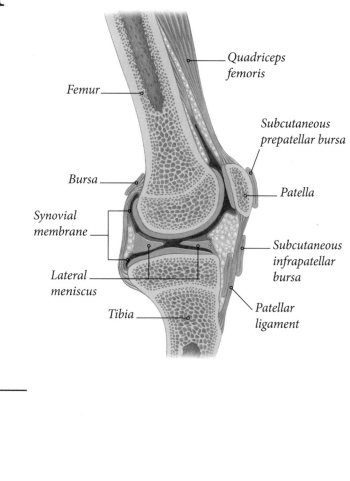

Femur

*Quadriceps
femoris*

*Subcutaneous
prepatellar bursa*

Bursa

Patella

*Synovial
membrane*

*Subcutaneous
infrapatellar
bursa*

*Lateral
meniscus*

Tibia

*Patellar
ligament*

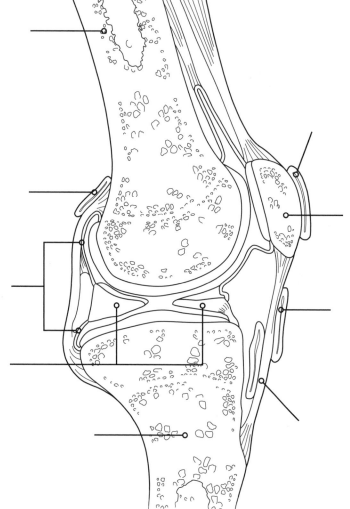

Inside the knee—the menisci

The menisci are
crescent-shaped plates
of tough fibrocartilage
lying on the articular
surface of the tibia. They
act as "shock absorbers"
within the knee and
prevent sideways
movement of the femur.

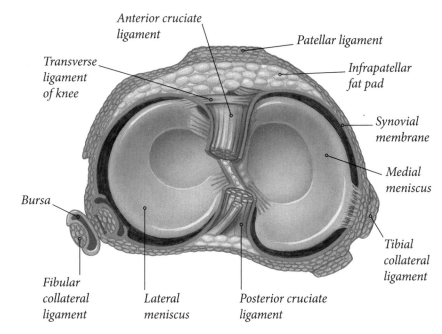

Anterior cruciate
ligament

Patellar ligament

Transverse
ligament
of knee

Infrapatellar
fat pad

Synovial
membrane

Medial
meniscus

Bursa

Tibial
collateral
ligament

Fibular
collateral
ligament

Lateral
meniscus

Posterior cruciate
ligament

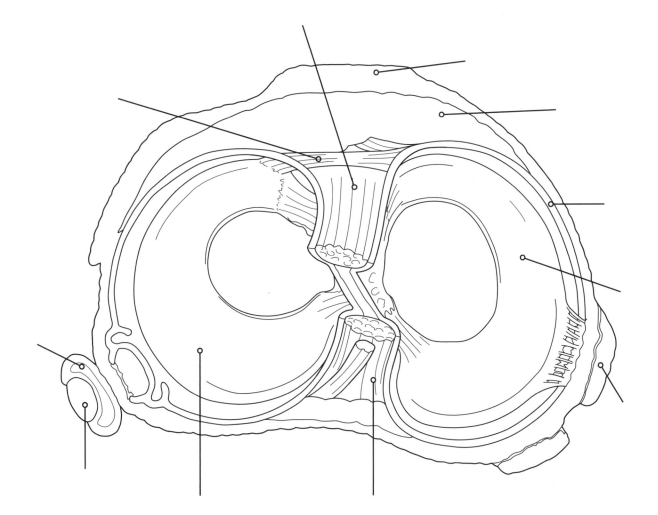

Ligaments of the knee

The knee joint is only partially enclosed in a capsule and relies on ligaments for its stability. Bursae are situated around the knee and allow smooth movement to take place.

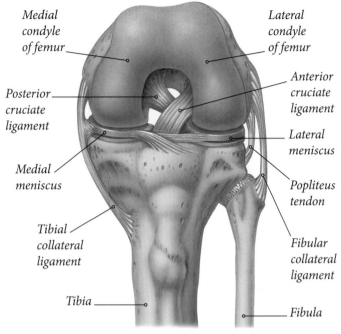

Medial condyle of femur

Lateral condyle of femur

Posterior cruciate ligament

Anterior cruciate ligament

Lateral meniscus

Medial meniscus

Popliteus tendon

Tibial collateral ligament

Fibular collateral ligament

Tibia

Fibula

ANTERIOR VIEW OF FLEXED LEFT KNEE

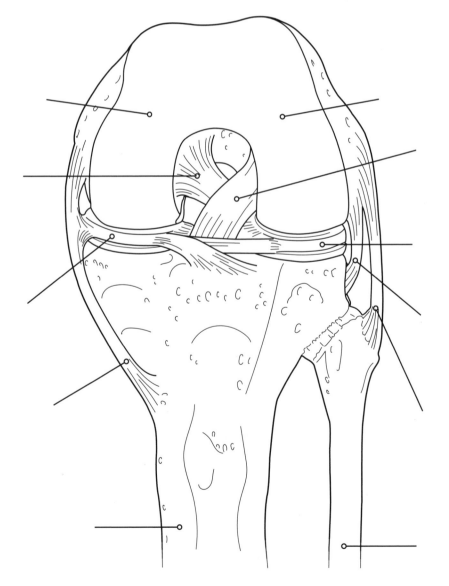

Bursae of the knee

The bursae of the knee are small sacs filled with synovial fluid. They act to protect the structures inside the knee, reducing friction, as they slide over each other when the joint is moving.

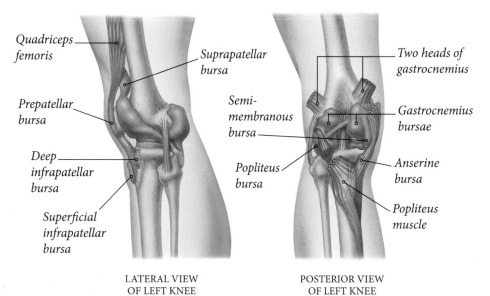

Quadriceps femoris

Suprapatellar bursa

Prepatellar bursa

Deep infrapatellar bursa

Superficial infrapatellar bursa

LATERAL VIEW
OF LEFT KNEE

Two heads of gastrocnemius

Semi-membranous bursa

Gastrocnemius bursae

Popliteus bursa

Anserine bursa

Popliteus muscle

POSTERIOR VIEW
OF LEFT KNEE

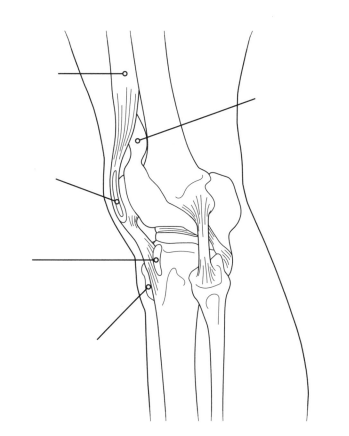

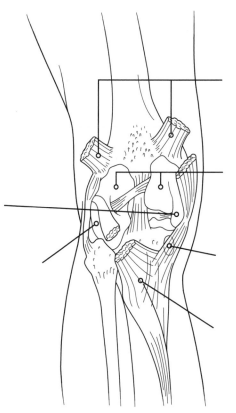

Muscles of the thigh

The thigh is composed mainly of groups of large muscles that act to move the hip and the knee joint. Muscles that effect the movements of the thigh are among the strongest in the body.

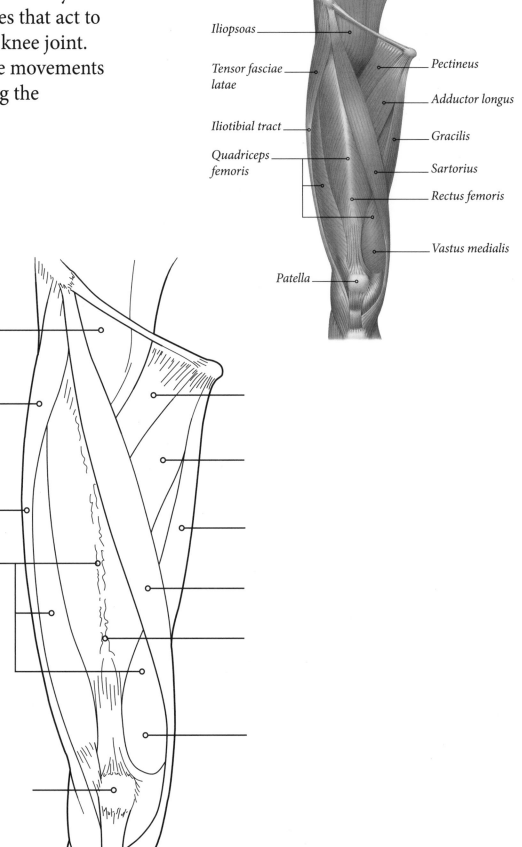

Iliopsoas

Tensor fasciae latae

Iliotibial tract

Quadriceps femoris

Patella

Pectineus

Adductor longus

Gracilis

Sartorius

Rectus femoris

Vastus medialis

Muscles of the lower leg

There are three groups of muscles in the lower leg. Depending where they lie, they support and flex the ankle and foot, extend the toes and assist in lifting the body weight at the heel.

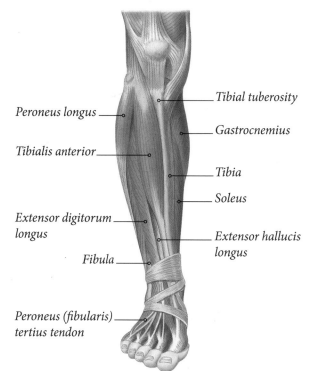

Peroneus longus

Tibialis anterior

Extensor digitorum longus

Fibula

Peroneus (fibularis) tertius tendon

Tibial tuberosity

Gastrocnemius

Tibia

Soleus

Extensor hallucis longus

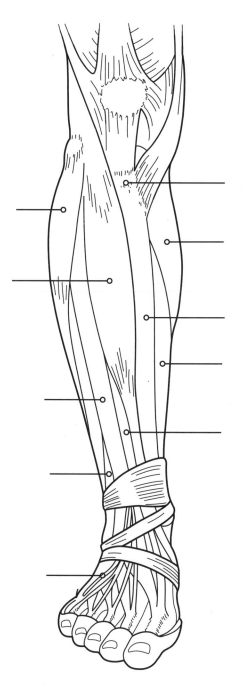

Posterior muscles of the lower leg

The posterior group of muscles of the lower leg form the mound of the calf. Together, these muscles are strong and heavy, enabling them to work together to flex the foot and to support the weight of the body.

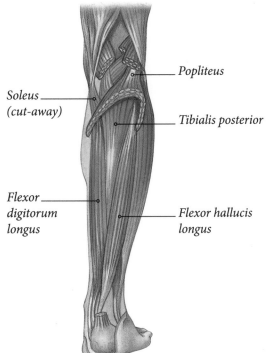

Soleus (cut-away)

Popliteus

Tibialis posterior

Flexor digitorum longus

Flexor hallucis longus

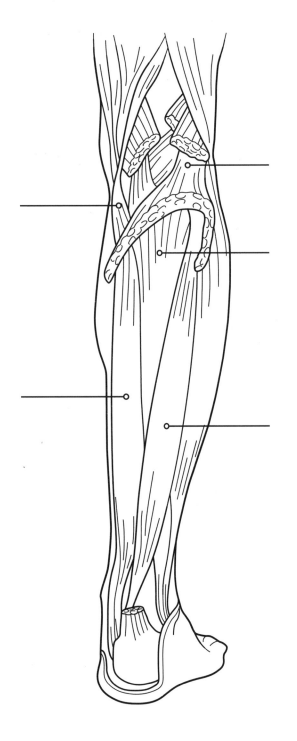

Arteries of the leg

The lower limb is supplied by a series of arteries that arise from the external iliac artery of the pelvis. These arteries pass down the leg, branching to reach muscles, bones, joints, and skin.

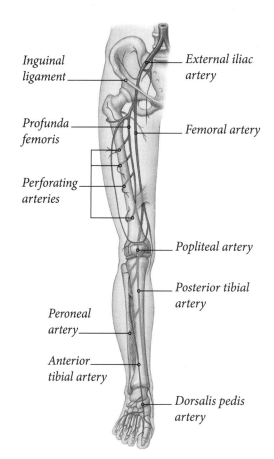

Inguinal ligament

External iliac artery

Profunda femoris

Femoral artery

Perforating arteries

Popliteal artery

Posterior tibial artery

Peroneal artery

Anterior tibial artery

Dorsalis pedis artery

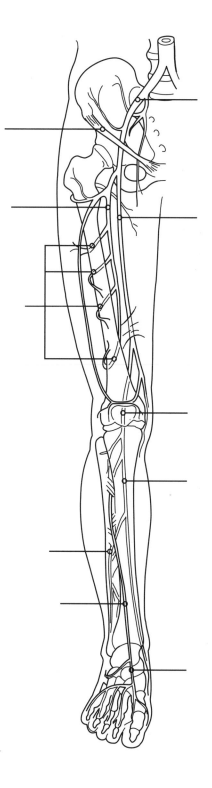

Arteries of the foot

In a pattern similar to that in the hand, the small arteries of the foot form arches that interconnect, giving off branches to each side of the toes. Branches of the arteries give the sole of the foot a particularly rich blood supply.

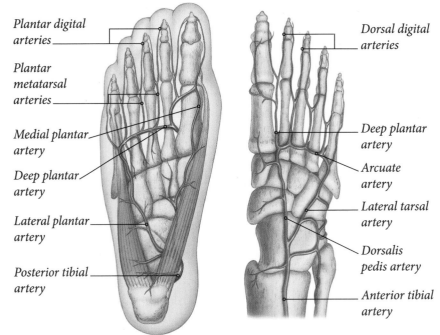

Plantar digital arteries

Plantar metatarsal arteries

Medial plantar artery

Deep plantar artery

Lateral plantar artery

Posterior tibial artery

Dorsal digital arteries

Deep plantar artery

Arcuate artery

Lateral tarsal artery

Dorsalis pedis artery

Anterior tibial artery

SOLE OF THE FOOT   TOP OF THE FOOT

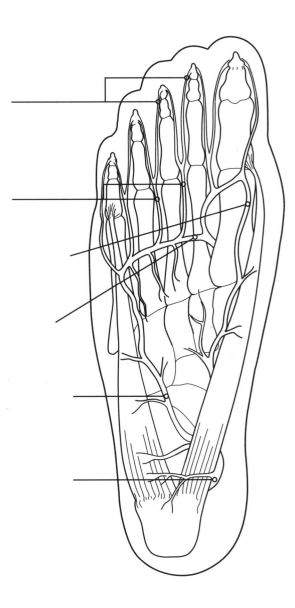

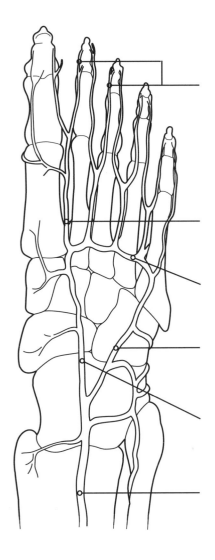

Veins of the leg

The lower limb is drained by a series of veins that can be divided into two groups, superficial and deep. The perforating veins connect the two groups of veins.

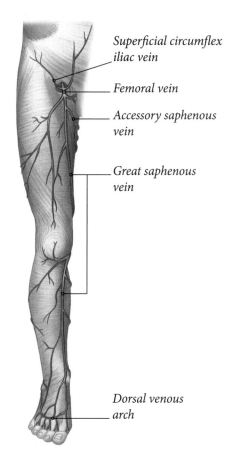

Superficial circumflex iliac vein

Femoral vein

Accessory saphenous vein

Great saphenous vein

Dorsal venous arch

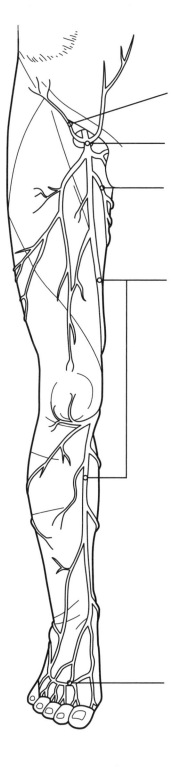

Deep veins of the leg

The deep veins of the leg follow the pattern of the arteries, which they accompany along their length. As well as draining venous blood from the tissues of the leg, the deep veins receive blood from the superficial veins via the perforating veins.

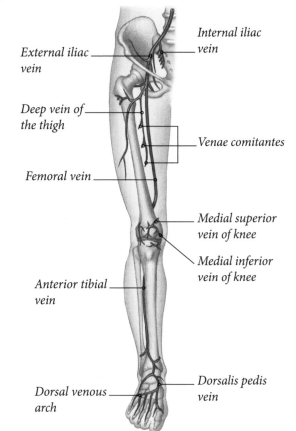

External iliac vein

Internal iliac vein

Deep vein of the thigh

Venae comitantes

Femoral vein

Medial superior vein of knee

Medial inferior vein of knee

Anterior tibial vein

Dorsal venous arch

Dorsalis pedis vein

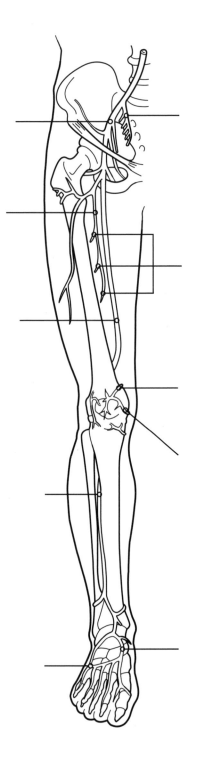

Nerves of the leg

The main nerve of the leg—the sciatic nerve—is the largest nerve in the body. Its branches supply the muscles of the hip, many of the thigh and all of the muscles of the lower leg and foot.

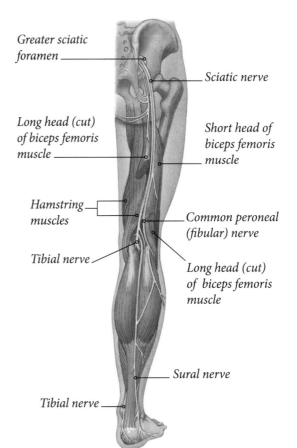

Greater sciatic foramen

Sciatic nerve

Long head (cut) of biceps femoris muscle

Short head of biceps femoris muscle

Hamstring muscles

Common peroneal (fibular) nerve

Tibial nerve

Long head (cut) of biceps femoris muscle

Sural nerve

Tibial nerve

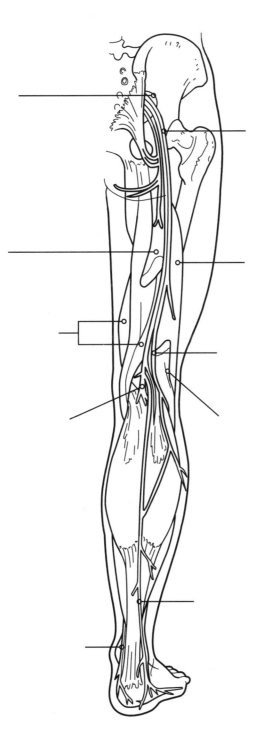

Terminal branches of the sciatic nerve

The sciatic nerve divides into two terminal branches: the common peroneal (fibular) nerve and the tibial nerve. The common peroneal nerve supplies the front of the leg, while the tibial nerve supplies the muscles and skin at the back.

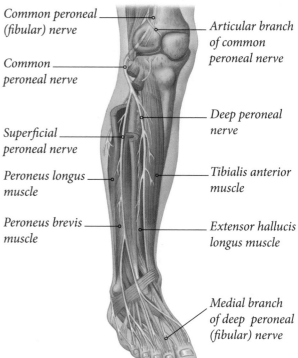

Common peroneal (fibular) nerve

Common peroneal nerve

Superficial peroneal nerve

Peroneus longus muscle

Peroneus brevis muscle

Articular branch of common peroneal nerve

Deep peroneal nerve

Tibialis anterior muscle

Extensor hallucis longus muscle

Medial branch of deep peroneal (fibular) nerve

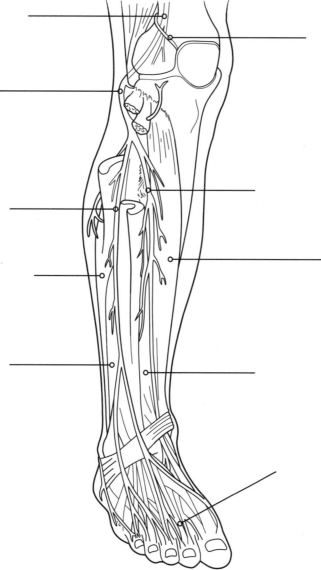

Ankle

The ankle is the joint between the lower ends of the tibia and fibula, and the upper surface of the large foot bone, the talus. It is an example of a hinge joint.

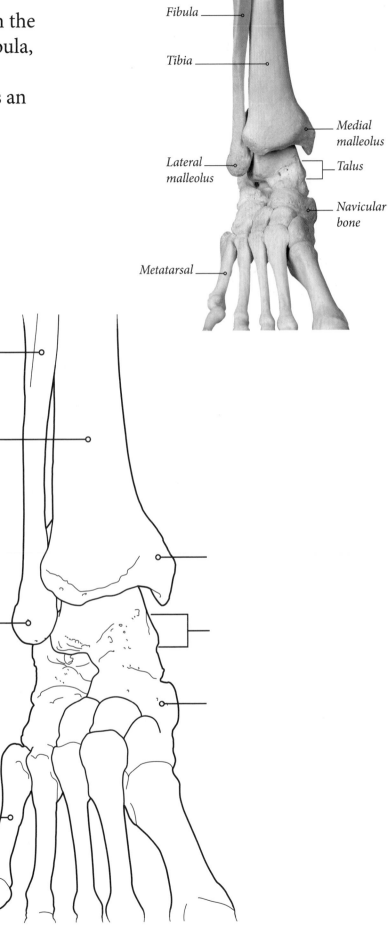

Fibula

Tibia

Medial malleolus

Lateral malleolus

Talus

Navicular bone

Metatarsal

Ligaments of the ankle

The ankle is supported
by strong ligaments
that help to stabilize
this important weight-
bearing joint.

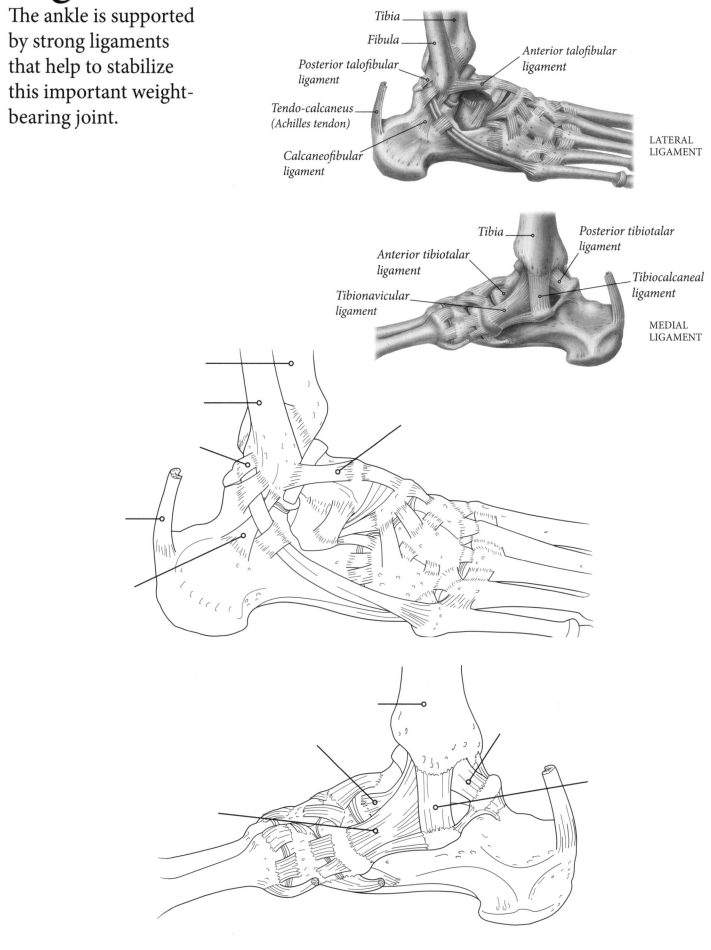

Tibia

Fibula

Posterior talofibular
ligament

Anterior talofibular
ligament

Tendo-calcaneus
(Achilles tendon)

Calcaneofibular
ligament

LATERAL
LIGAMENT

Tibia

Posterior tibiotalar
ligament

Anterior tibiotalar
ligament

Tibionavicular
ligament

Tibiocalcaneal
ligament

MEDIAL
LIGAMENT

Bones of the foot

The human foot has 26 bones in total: seven larger, irregular tarsal bones; five metatarsals running the length of the foot; and 14 phalanges forming the skeleton of the toes.

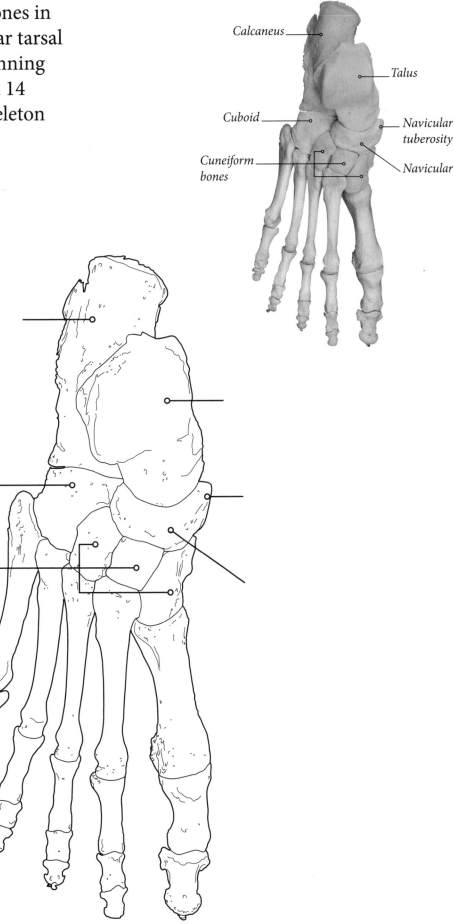

Calcaneus

Talus

Cuboid

Navicular tuberosity

Cuneiform bones

Navicular

Metatarsals and phalanges

The metatarsals and phalanges in the foot are miniature long bones, consisting of a base, shaft, and head.

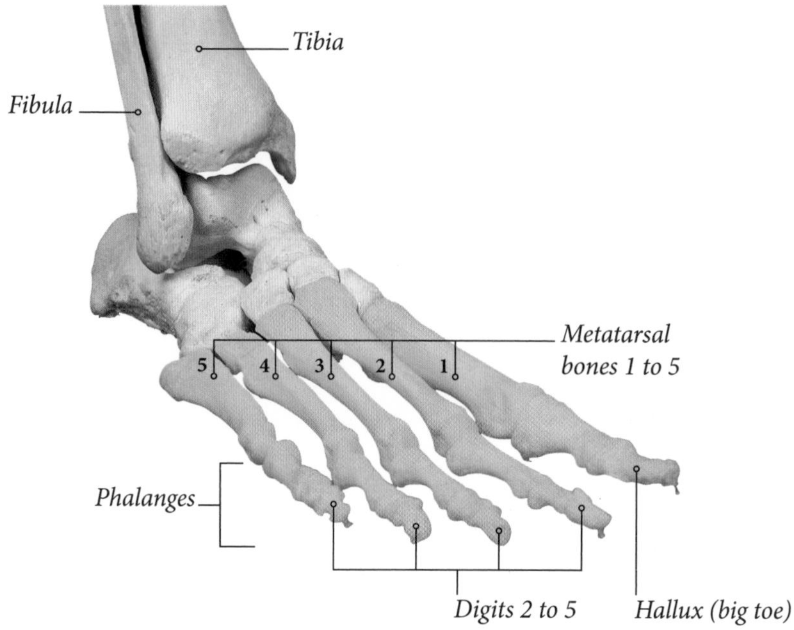

Tibia

Fibula

Metatarsal bones 1 to 5

5   4   3   2   1

Phalanges

Digits 2 to 5

Hallux (big toe)

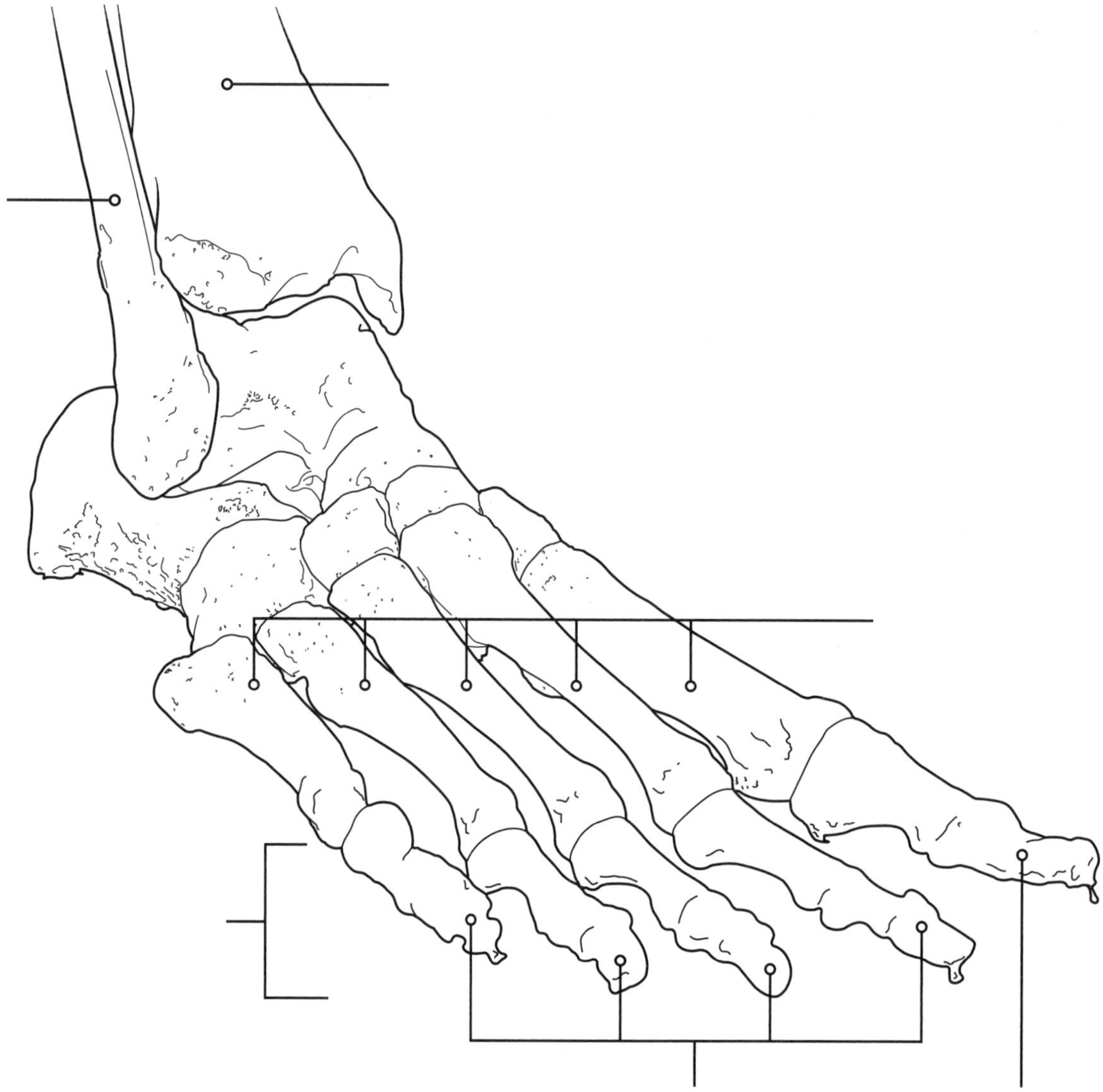

Ligaments of the foot

The bones of the foot are arranged
in such a way that they form
bridge-like arches. These bones
are supported by the presence of a
number of strong ligaments.

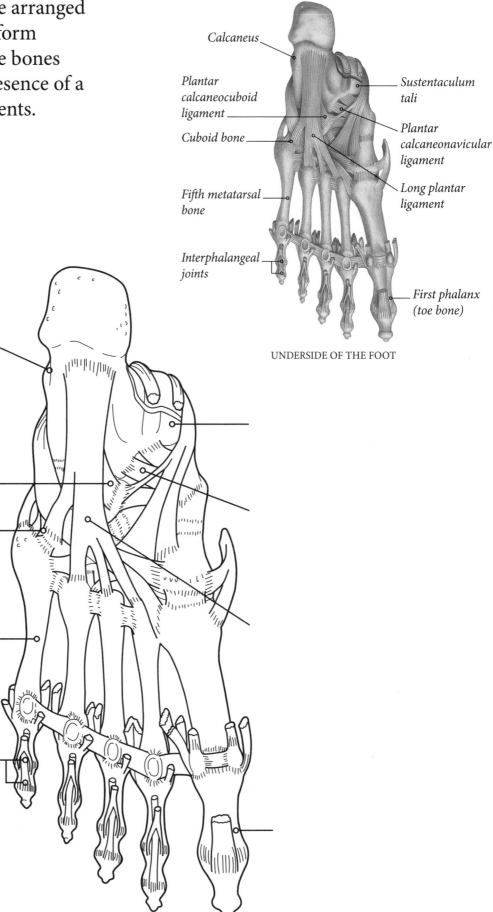

Calcaneus

Plantar
calcaneocuboid
ligament

Cuboid bone

Fifth metatarsal
bone

Interphalangeal
joints

Sustentaculum
tali

Plantar
calcaneonavicular
ligament

Long plantar
ligament

First phalanx
(toe bone)

UNDERSIDE OF THE FOOT

Arches of the foot

A distinctive feature of the human foot is that the bones within it are arranged in bridge-like arches. This allows the foot to be flexible enough to cope with uneven ground, while still being able to bear the weight of the body.

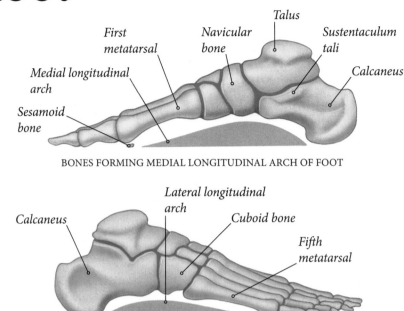

First metatarsal
Talus
Navicular bone
Sustentaculum tali
Medial longitudinal arch
Calcaneus
Sesamoid bone

BONES FORMING MEDIAL LONGITUDINAL ARCH OF FOOT

Lateral longitudinal arch
Calcaneus
Cuboid bone
Fifth metatarsal

BONES FORMING LATERAL LONGITUDINAL ARCH OF FOOT

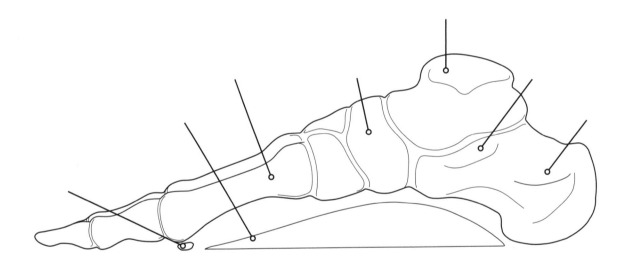

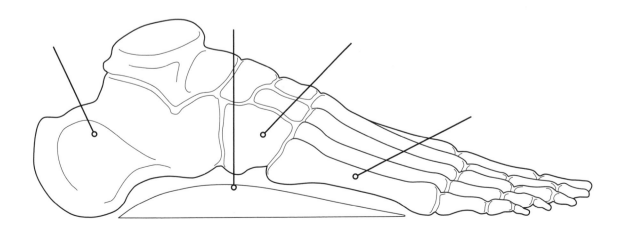

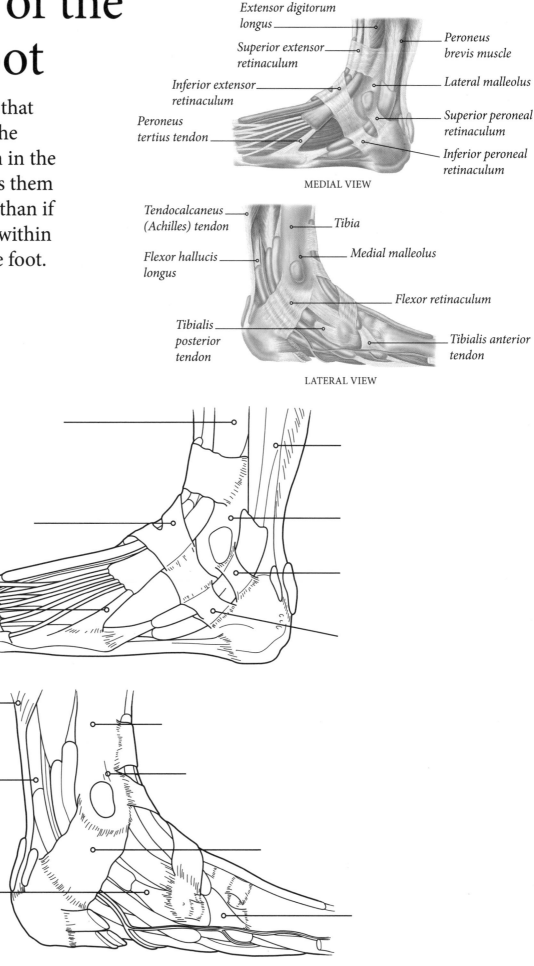

Muscles of the upper foot

Many of the muscles that move the foot lie in the lower leg, rather than in the foot itself. This allows them to be more powerful than if they were contained within the small space of the foot.

Extensor digitorum longus

Superior extensor retinaculum

Inferior extensor retinaculum

Peroneus tertius tendon

Peroneus brevis muscle

Lateral malleolus

Superior peroneal retinaculum

Inferior peroneal retinaculum

MEDIAL VIEW

Tendocalcaneus (Achilles) tendon

Flexor hallucis longus

Tibialis posterior tendon

Tibia

Medial malleolus

Flexor retinaculum

Tibialis anterior tendon

LATERAL VIEW

Muscles of the top of the foot

Although they are not particularly powerful, the muscles that lie over the top of the foot play an important part in helping to extend the toes.

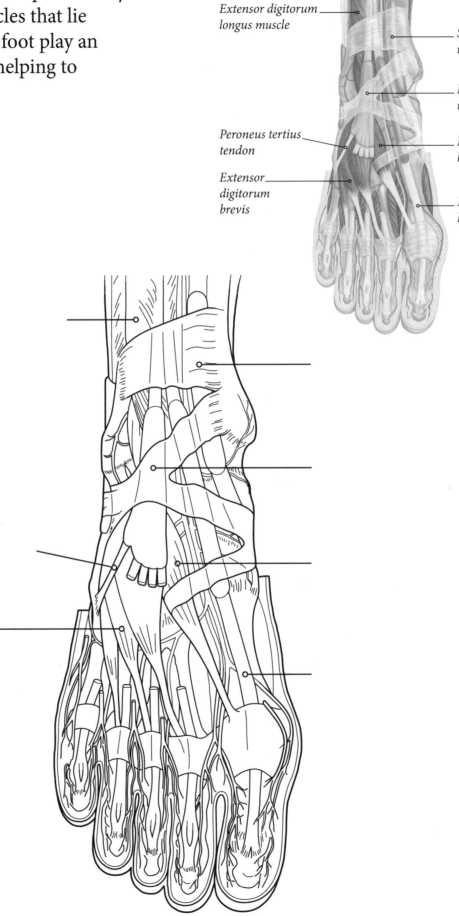

Extensor digitorum longus muscle

Superior extensor retinaculum

Inferior extensor retinaculum

Peroneus tertius tendon

Extensor digitorum brevis

Extensor hallucis brevis

Extensor hallucis longus tendon

Muscles of the sole of the foot

Many of the movements of the
bones and joints of the feet are
brought about by muscles in the
lower leg. However, there are also
many small "intrinsic" muscles
that lie entirely within the foot.

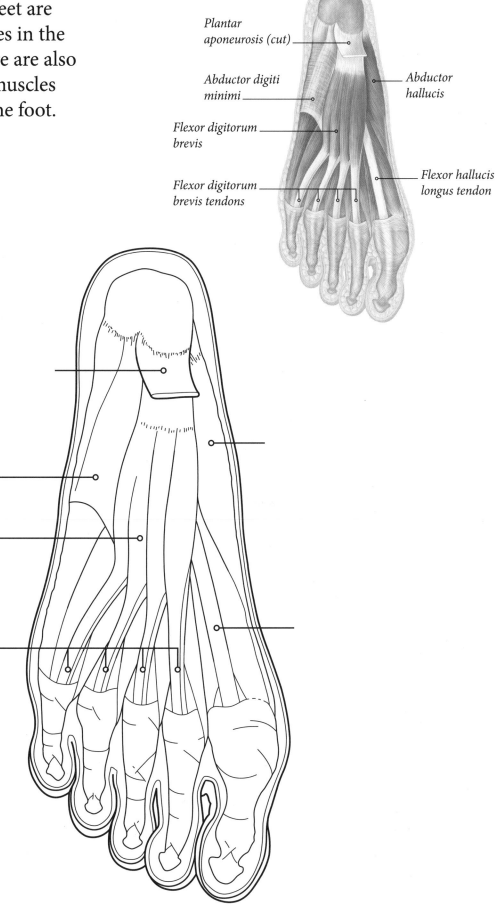

*Plantar
aponeurosis (cut)*

*Abductor digiti
minimi*

*Flexor digitorum
brevis*

*Flexor digitorum
brevis tendons*

*Abductor
hallucis*

*Flexor hallucis
longus tendon*

The skeleton

The skeleton is made up of bone and cartilage, and it accounts for one-fifth of the body's weight. Over 200 bones form a living structure, superbly designed to support and protect the body.

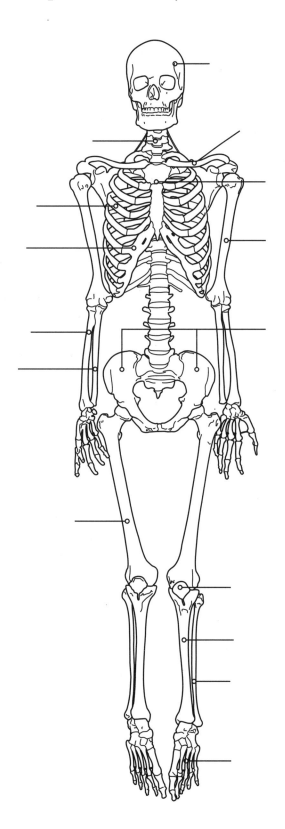

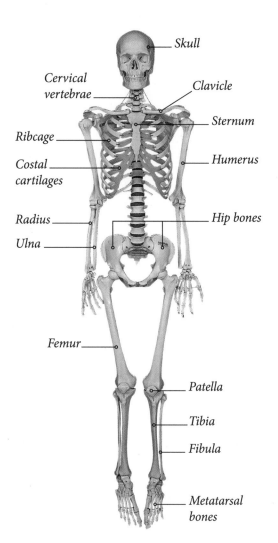

Skull

Cervical vertebrae

Clavicle

Sternum

Ribcage

Costal cartilages

Humerus

Radius

Ulna

Hip bones

Femur

Patella

Tibia

Fibula

Metatarsal bones

Types of joints

A joint is formed where two
or more bones meet. Some
allow movement and so give
mobility to the body while
others protect and support
the body by holding the bones
rigid against one another.

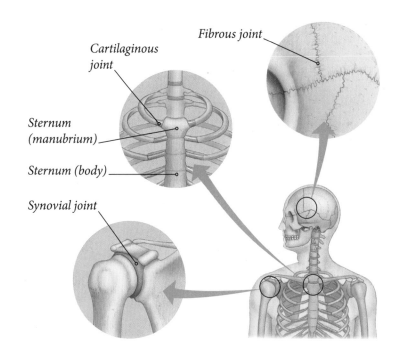

Fibrous joint

*Cartilaginous
joint*

*Sternum
(manubrium)*

Sternum (body)

Synovial joint

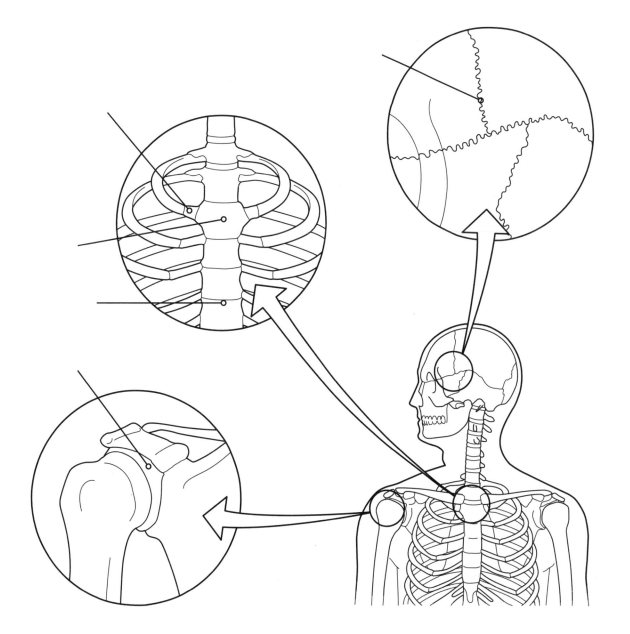

Types of muscle

There are three main types of muscle in the body—skeletal muscle is used for voluntary movement, smooth muscle controls internal organs, and cardiac muscle keeps the heart beating.

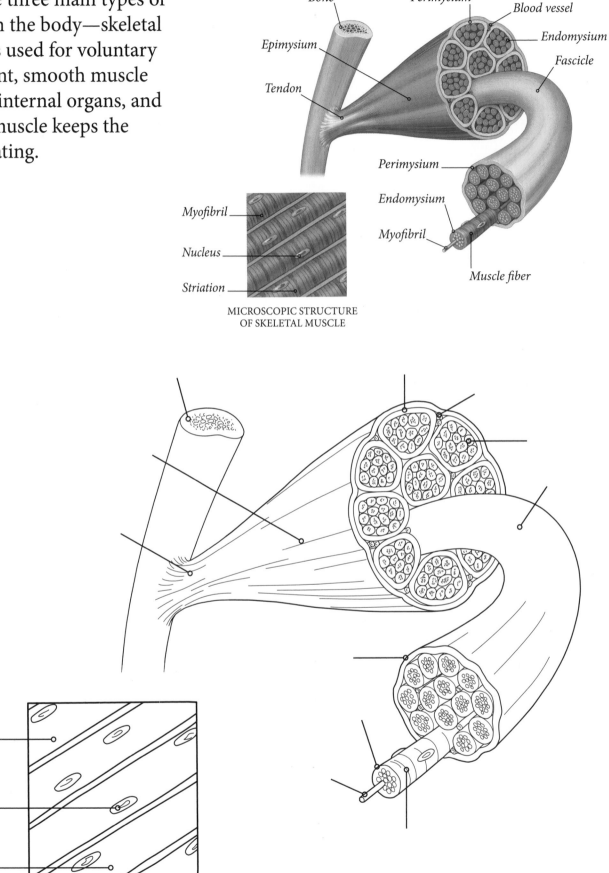

Bone

Perimysium

Blood vessel

Epimysium

Endomysium

Tendon

Fascicle

Perimysium

Endomysium

Myofibril

Myofibril

Nucleus

Striation

Muscle fiber

MICROSCOPIC STRUCTURE
OF SKELETAL MUSCLE

Shapes of skeletal muscle

Although all skeletal muscles are
made up of fascicles, or groups of
muscle fibers, the arrangement of these
fascicles may vary. This variation leads
to a number of different muscle shapes
throughout the body.

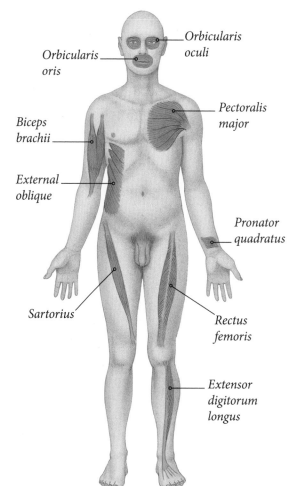

*Orbicularis
oris*

*Orbicularis
oculi*

*Biceps
brachii*

*Pectoralis
major*

*External
oblique*

*Pronator
quadratus*

Sartorius

*Rectus
femoris*

*Extensor
digitorum
longus*

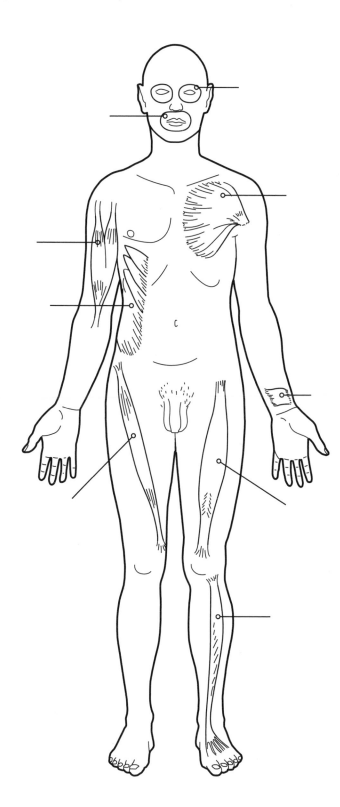

Overview of blood circulation

There are two blood vessel networks in the body. The pulmonary circulation transports blood between the heart and lungs; the systemic circulation supplies blood to all parts except the lungs.

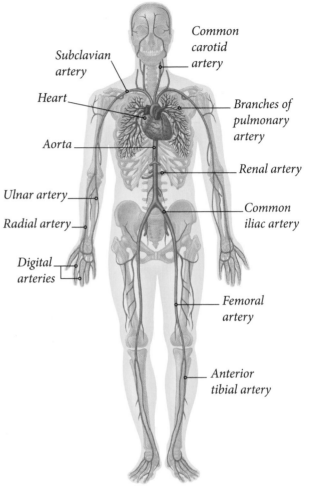

Subclavian artery

Common carotid artery

Heart

Branches of pulmonary artery

Aorta

Renal artery

Ulnar artery

Radial artery

Common iliac artery

Digital arteries

Femoral artery

Anterior tibial artery

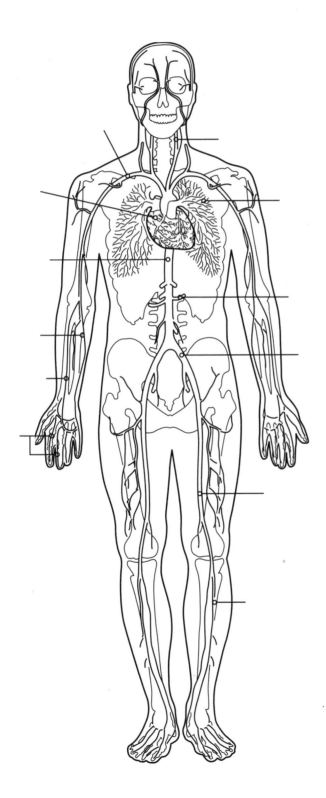

Venous system

The venous system carries blood back to the heart from the tissues. This blood is then pumped through the pulmonary circulation to be reoxygenated before entering the systemic circulation again.

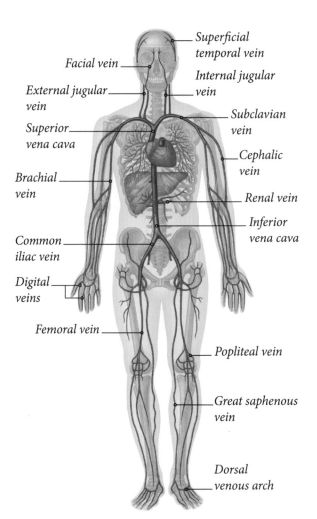

Superficial temporal vein

Facial vein

Internal jugular vein

External jugular vein

Subclavian vein

Superior vena cava

Cephalic vein

Brachial vein

Renal vein

Inferior vena cava

Common iliac vein

Digital veins

Femoral vein

Popliteal vein

Great saphenous vein

Dorsal venous arch

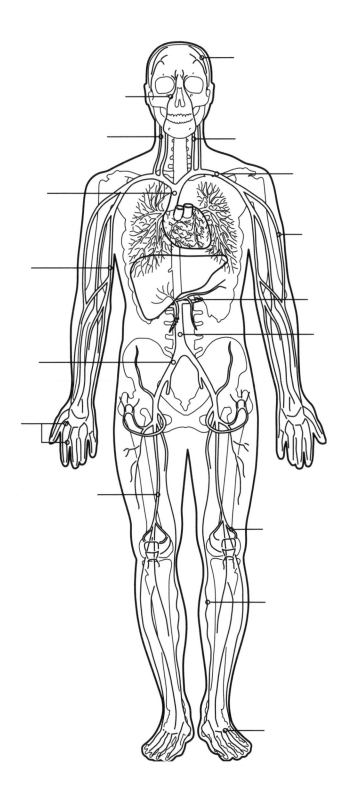

Peripheral nervous system

The peripheral nervous system includes all the body's nerve tissue that is not in the brain and spinal cord. Its principal anatomical components are the cranial and spinal nerves.

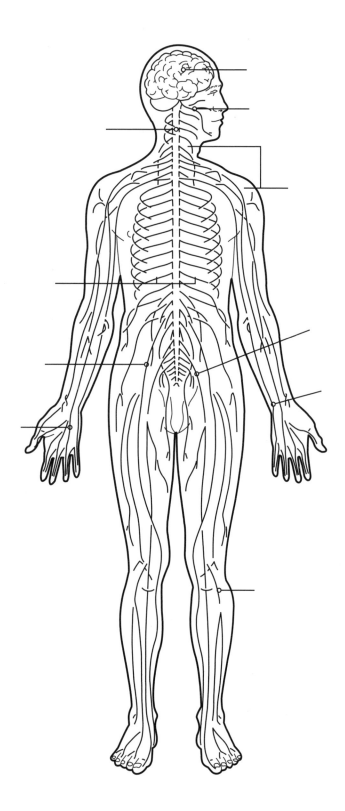

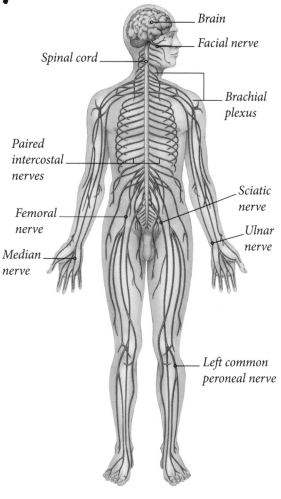

Brain

Facial nerve

Spinal cord

Brachial plexus

Paired intercostal nerves

Femoral nerve

Median nerve

Sciatic nerve

Ulnar nerve

Left common peroneal nerve

Structure of a peripheral nerve

Each peripheral nerve consists
of separate nerve fibers,
some with an insulating layer
of myelin, enclosed within
connective tissue.

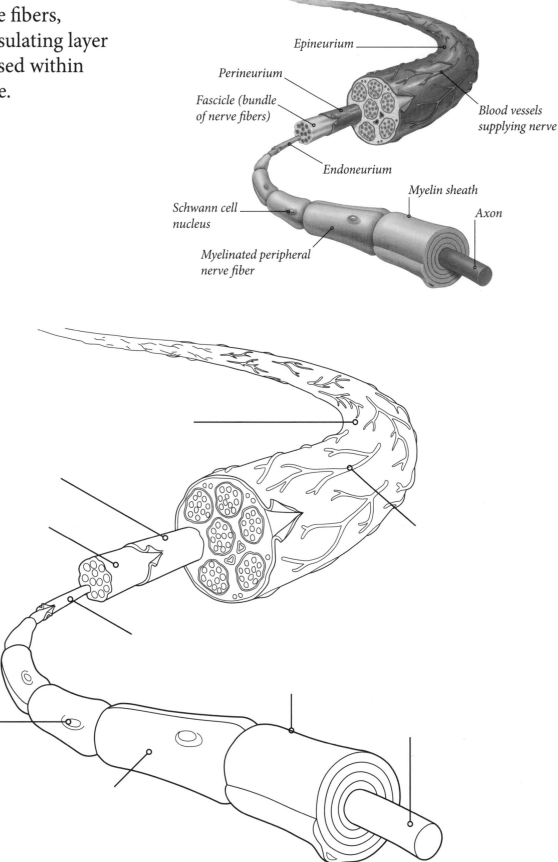

Epineurium

Perineurium

*Fascicle (bundle
of nerve fibers)*

*Blood vessels
supplying nerve*

Endoneurium

Myelin sheath

Axon

*Schwann cell
nucleus*

*Myelinated peripheral
nerve fiber*

Autonomic nervous system

The autonomic nervous system provides the nerve supply to those parts of the body that are not consciously directed. It can be subdivided into the sympathetic and parasympathetic systems.

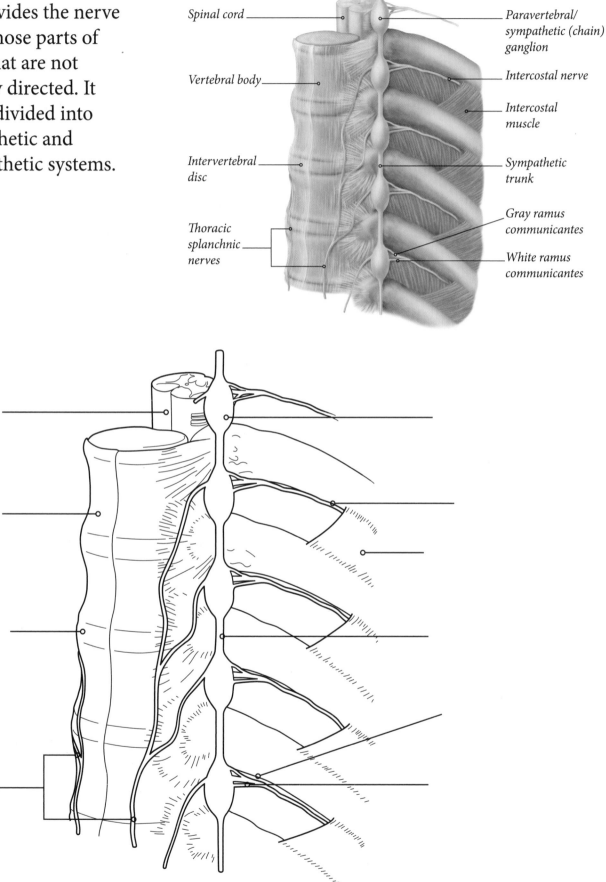

Spinal cord

Vertebral body

Intervertebral disc

Thoracic splanchnic nerves

Paravertebral/ sympathetic (chain) ganglion

Intercostal nerve

Intercostal muscle

Sympathetic trunk

Gray ramus communicantes

White ramus communicantes

Lymphatic system

The lymphatic system consists of a network of lymph vessels and organs and specialized cells throughout the body. It is an essential part of the body's defense against invading microorganisms.

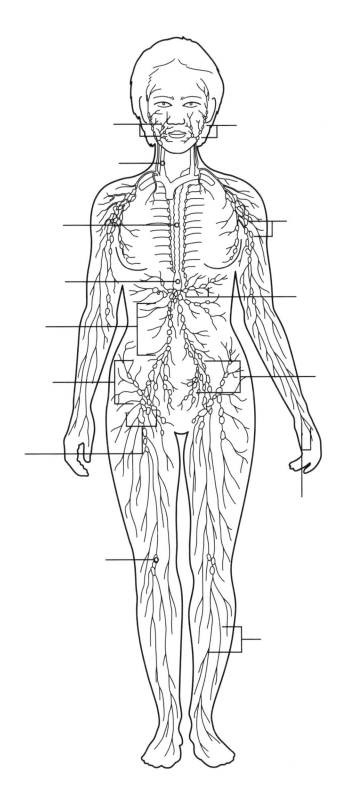

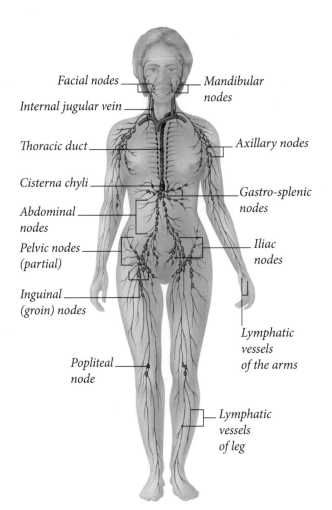

Facial nodes

Mandibular nodes

Internal jugular vein

Axillary nodes

Thoracic duct

Cisterna chyli

Gastro-splenic nodes

Abdominal nodes

Pelvic nodes (partial)

Iliac nodes

Inguinal (groin) nodes

Lymphatic vessels of the arms

Popliteal node

Lymphatic vessels of leg

Lymph nodes

Lymph nodes lie along
the route of the lymphatic
vessels. They filter the
lymph for invading
microorganisms, infected
cells and also other
foreign particles.

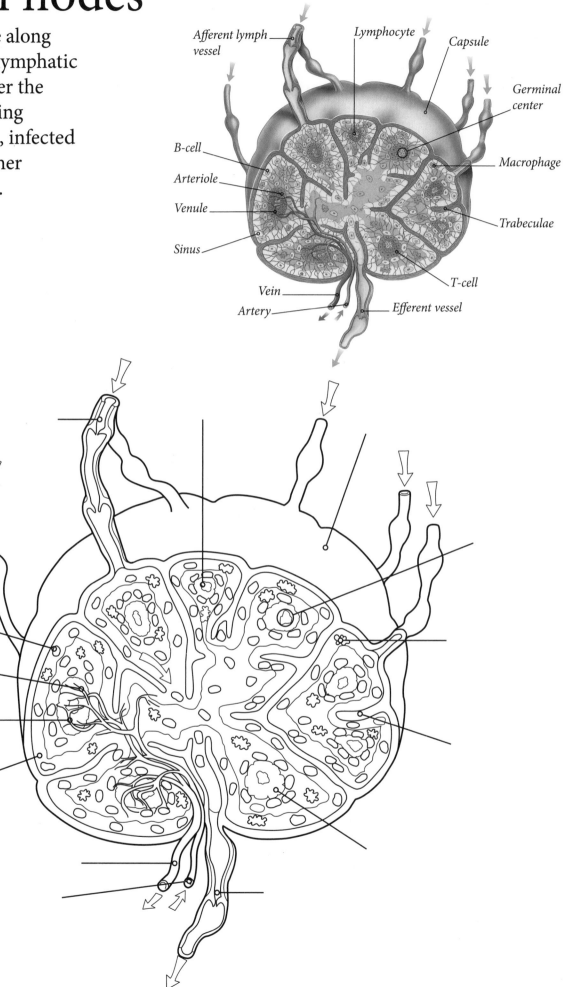

Afferent lymph
vessel

Lymphocyte

Capsule

Germinal
center

B-cell

Arteriole

Venule

Sinus

Macrophage

Trabeculae

Vein

Artery

T-cell

Efferent vessel

Skin

The skin, together with the hair and nails, makes up the integumentary system. Functions of the skin include heat regulation and defense against microbial attack.

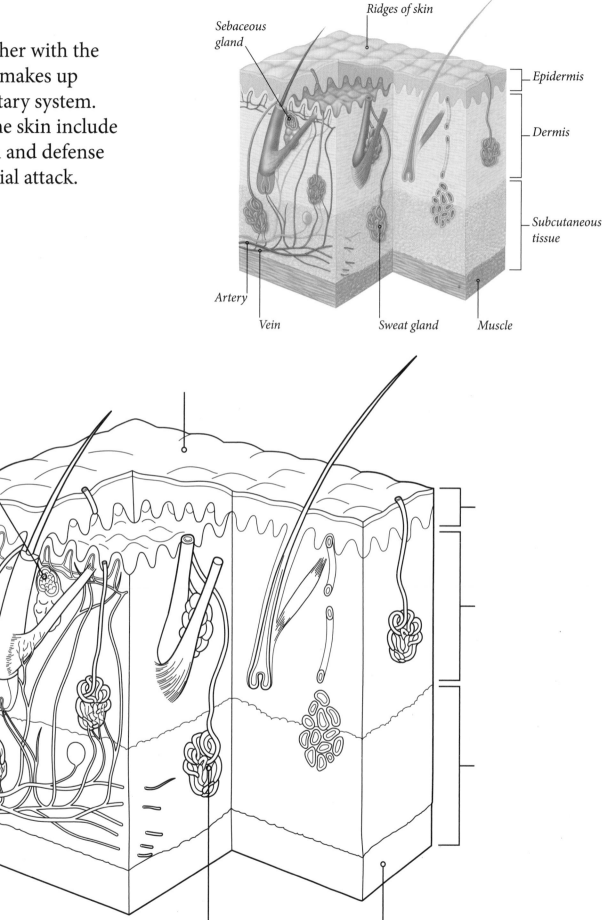

Sebaceous gland

Ridges of skin

Epidermis

Dermis

Subcutaneous tissue

Artery

Vein

Sweat gland

Muscle

Nails

Human nails are the equivalent of the hooves or claws of other animals. They form a hard protective covering for the vulnerable fingers and toes, and they provide a useful tool for scratching or scraping when this is required.

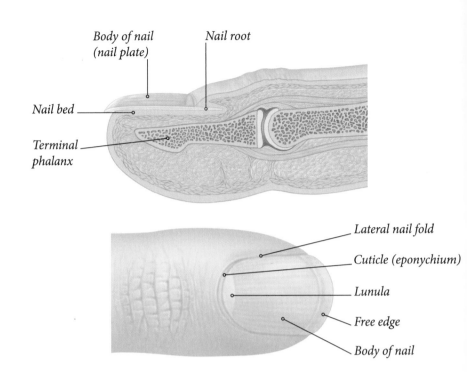

Body of nail (nail plate)

Nail root

Nail bed

Terminal phalanx

Lateral nail fold

Cuticle (eponychium)

Lunula

Free edge

Body of nail

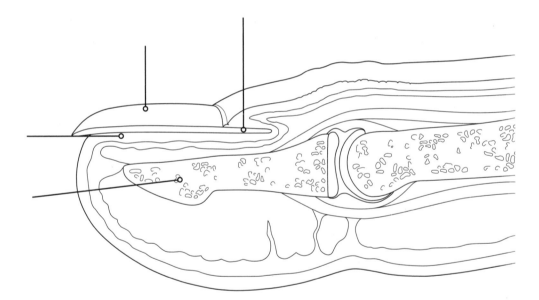

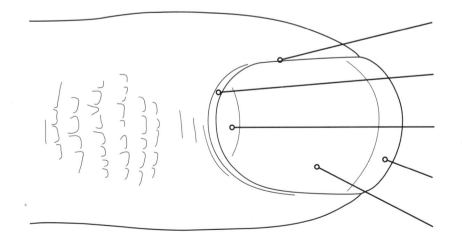

Index